D1213239

Books by ALFRED BESTER

WHO HE?
THE DEMOLISHED MAN
THE STARS MY DESTINATION
STARBURST
THE DARK SIDE OF THE EARTH
THE LIFE AND DEATH OF A SATELLITE

The Life and Death of a Satellite

The Life and Death of a Satellite

by ALFRED BESTER

with photographs

Little, Brown and Company • Boston • Toronto

LIBRARY OF CONGRESS CATALOG CARD NO. 66-22677

FIRST EDITION

The lines by T. S. Eliot on page 120 are from "The Hollow Men" from *Collected Poems 1909-1962* by T. S. Eliot, and are reprinted by kind permission of the publishers, Harcourt, Brace & World, Inc., and Faber and Faber Ltd.

Published simultaneously in Canada
by Little, Brown & Company (Canada) Limited

PRINTED IN THE UNITED STATES OF AMERICA

This book is dedicated to the men and women of NASA, with admiration and affection.

Contents

The Life and Death of a Satellite

1

Men vs. Machines in Space

After the Ranger probes sent back their spectacular close-ups of the moon, a friend of mine, a very bright guy who'd taken an arts degree at a Midwestern university, asked a rather naïve question. He wanted to know why they had to go to all that trouble to photograph the moon. Why couldn't they have taken the pictures from earth, using giant flashbulbs? While I was trying to unravel the mysteries of flash photography, light transmission, and lens resolution for him, I realized that the average intelligent adult understands very little about the fascinating research conducted by our space program; in fact, he understands far less than his ten-year-old son.

There are many reasons for this. He has never had the space program explained to him from behind the scenes, and in ordinary language. Space science has developed such a special vocabulary that the layman finds it impossible to follow. There are times when I suspect the scientists and engineers of deliberately fostering this language barrier. At other times I realize that they're so wrapped up in their specialties that it never occurs to them that the rest of the world doesn't speak their tongue. Certainly too many popular science writers, who should translate for the layman, become hypnotized by the technical terms and abandon plain speaking altogether.

The result is that most intelligent people make no attempt to acquaint themselves with the actual workings of the space program because they feel they're licked before they start. After a few exposures to descriptions and explanations bristling with such terms as "redundant power system" (which means spare batteries) they give up in disgust, and I don't blame them.

But none of this technical language is really necessary or, if it is, utterly untranslatable. Most space terms have their equivalents in everyday language, and can be translated into common speech. I intend to make such a translation in this biography of the men and machines fighting an exciting war with the most hostile and unyielding enemy man has ever faced, space. It's not yet a battle for space travel. The Manned Space Flight program is still only a minor skirmish in preparation for that future encounter. The present war, the major war, is a battle to wring information from space.

Contrary to the general impression produced by newspaper headlines and TV coverage, our space program is not an all-out effort to beat the Russians to the moon. It's a carefully planned program of research and discovery; a sort of modern Lewis and Clark Expedition. This is a fair analogy. After the Louisiana Purchase, President Jefferson wanted to find out all he could about the thousands of miles of territory which he'd just bought. He didn't send Lewis and Clark on a hike. They were sent out with every available scientific instrument to do an exhaustive survey.

Today we're trying to discover all we can about the millions of miles of space around our earth, and are sending up every available scientific instrument to do the survey.

Now many people have a romantic misconception of scientific research and discovery, produced for the most part by movie versions of the lives of Pasteur, Edison, Ehrlich, *et al.* We all know the pat scenario; Vision, Opposition, Lucky Accident, Vindication. S. J. Perelman reduced this formula to its final absurdity in his re-creation of the invention of the electric blanket:

> I can readily imagine some brilliant young chemist bursting into the office of the head of the division, exultantly waving a test tube. "What's cooking, Shaftoe — I mean Muni?" inquires his chief irritably. "Another one of those impractical daydreams of yours?" "N-n-no, sir," stammers Shaftoe in his excitement. "Do you recall that precipitate of blanketane, comfortate cellulose, and old voltage I left on my bench last night?" "Yes, it was the seven-hundred-and-forty-fifth combination that you and Bazurdjian had tried, and although all others failed, you doggedly persisted, scorning the mockery of older and wiser heads," replies the chief. "Look here, sir!" cries Shaftoe, holding the test tube up to the light. "My God!" exclaims his usually imperturbable senior. "A little electrical quilt! Imperfect, incomplete, picayune, but still a quilt. What formula did you use, my boy?" "A very old one, sir," says Shaftoe quietly. "One part inspiration and ten of perspiration."

As a rule, discoveries aren't made that way. They're more often the result of the interaction of theory and technology. For example, Columbus's voyage in 1492, which was the great space exploration of the Middle Ages, wasn't any attempt to prove that the world was round, as we were taught in grammar school. It was the direct result of a furious geographers' dispute, and advances in the technique of navigation which enabled mariners at last to sail out of the sight of land.

The theoreticians of the time knew damn well that the world was round; they agreed on that. What they couldn't agree on was its size. There was a Big Earth faction and a Small Earth faction, and neither could come up with experimental proof of its theory. Columbus belonged to the Small Earth crowd, which is why he was convinced that India was on the other side of the Atlantic. He accepted Claudius Ptolemy's figure for the circumference of the earth, which was short by seven thousand miles. Among other things, his voyage was an experiment to test a theory. The fact that his theory was wrong, and he wound up discovering something he wasn't looking for, makes him seem real contemporary.

Dr. Bill Hess of the Goddard Space Flight Center says, "But you have to understand that the theorist doesn't tell the experimental scientist to do scientific experiments. They work simultaneously. Experimenters are always experimenting. Theorists are constantly building theoretical models. One buys Geiger counters; the other buys pencils. The theorist looks around for experimental data to support his theory. If there isn't any, he publishes and waits. The experimenter reads the publication and maybe alters an existing experiment to test the theory."

In this relationship theory must usually wait on technique. Perhaps the classic example of this is the history of the computer, and the computer is as essential to the space age as rocketry. Theorists had been speculating about computer design for three hundred years, and engineers had been building experimental machines, culminating in the mid-nineteenth century with Charles Babbage's beautiful "Calculating Engine" which he was never able to finish. It was not until the twentieth century that engineering techniques advanced enough to make it possible to implement and test the theories. By then, theory was on the march again, once more waiting for technique to catch up.

J. Presper Eckert, who, with Dr. John Mauchly, built ENIAC, the very first electronic computer, gives the engineer's point of view on this relationship. He says, "They [the theorists] were brilliant guys who exploded with ideas in all directions, but this doesn't count. You have to buckle down, build it, and make it work. This is their weakness; they flash ideas which are not really workable. Once Norbert Wiener suggested a rather delicate idea to me and I said it was good but impractical. Wiener was astonished. He said, 'But I'm a practical man. I drive a car to work every morning.' "

On the other hand, the theorist hopes that what's impractical today will be practical tomorrow. For a hundred years physicists and astronomers had been aware of strange phenomena in the space around our earth. They agreed that the phenomena existed, but could not agree on the interpretation, and since they were earthbound there was no practical way of testing their theories. Like the geographers of Columbus's time they were forced to wait until the technique of navigation — in this case, space navigation — had advanced enough to enable them to put instruments up there and collect experimental data.

Perhaps you've noticed that my main emphasis is on instruments. This is because the main interest of the scientists involved in our space program lies in research and discovery by instrument, not in manned spacecraft. Instrumental research is an ideal collaboration of science and engineering; the engineer provides the technique by which the scientist can acquire experimental data. The Manned Spacecraft program is solely an engineering project; the engineering is the end in itself.

NASA (the National Aeronautics and Space Administration) and the armed forces are launching some fifty major spacecraft a year from Cape Kennedy. Most public attention is focused on the Manned Spacecraft program, which is only natural; it has produced some of the most dramatic events in the history of adventure. But the truth is that these events, which take place at irregular intervals, are only the glamorous window dressing of the space program. The real work, the bread-and-butter work, is being done by the scientific spacecraft.

The Manned Spacecraft program admits that up to the Gemini missions it was accomplishing very little of any real scientific value. All it was trying to do was develop craft for future space exploration, and adapt astronauts to the craft. The Gemini missions are flying experiments, and the Apollo mission is training scientists to act as scientist-astronauts. Nevertheless, the program has not received one hundred per cent endorsement.

Many scientists ask, "But what will man explore? If you land a man on the moon all he can do is walk around for a few hours, pick up a few samples, and then get the hell off as quickly as possible. The Mars and Venus probes have revealed that man can't survive on these inhospitable planets, and we already know that the gassy outer planets are hopeless for exploration. So far as the stars are concerned, it would take lifetimes to reach them."

Even the NASA engineers are split on the issue. One school asks, "Why spend billions to send man into space when, from the mechanical standpoint, machines can do anything a man can do, do it better, do it more completely, and at one-fiftieth of the cost?"

The Man-in-Space school argues, "No, man is adaptable. He can meet and do the unexpected. He can repair equipment if it breaks down. And only man can pilot the Apollo mission to the moon."

The Machine-in-Space school replies, "Absolutely not! If he sticks a screwdriver into a piece of equipment he'll ruin it. And the only safe way for him to pilot the craft is to put him out with a sleeping pill and let the automatic machines take over."

Dr. Albert Hibbs of the Jet Propulsion Laboratory (this is the same Hibbs who made headlines when he used mathematics to beat the gambling tables at Las Vegas) says, "The debate is unrealistic because man is controlling the machine at all times. There's always a man pushing the button somewhere; it's just a question of where in the loop you find him. The only difference is how near he is to the hardware, geographically.

"In manned satellites, for example, the pilot is technically unnecessary. Computers on earth decide when to fire the retrorockets, which could be fired automatically. All the pilot does is receive the radio signal from earth and push a button to activate the craft computer. He could be replaced by a relay because the man in charge is the one working the computer on the ground."

About man in space, Hibbs says he has a fantasy of the

first astronaut on the moon being interviewed from earth by radio. He's afraid the conversation will go something like this:

"What's it like to be the first man on the moon?"

"It's wonderful! Just wonderful! I wouldn't have missed this for the world!"

"Well, what's the moon like?"

"It's wonderful! And I want to thank all those guys, all those scientists, who made this wonderful experience possible!"

"Yes, but what does the moon look like?"

"It looks just wonderful. I can see the earth very clearly, and it looks wonderful, too!"

"But what's the moon *like?*"

"Well . . . It's kind of rocky."

Hibbs smiled. "I think that all men in space can do is describe their sensations and emotions, which is why I think we should launch poets instead of pilots. Scientific research is not really the prime purpose of the manned space program; it's to satisfy the curiosity and adventuring spirit of man. But there's another possibility. Professor Tommy Gold of Cornell has developed the 'Rotten Tomato Theory.'

"A billion years ago spacemen came to earth from another star. They came for the usual purposes: exploration, scientific examination, and military reconnaissance. They found an inhospitable planet with a methane and ammonia atmosphere. They realized it wasn't suitable for settling so they left and moved on.

"But before they left they dumped their garbage disposal units. Bacteria from the garbage thrived in that environment and evolved into our life. Now we're starting the same program and will probably do the same thing on another planet of another star. Maybe this is the real purpose of the space program. We're just the tools of bacteria to infect the universe."

And while the Man vs. Machine debate seesaws between humor and rancor, the scientific satellites quietly go about their business of collecting priceless information about the earth and its environment in space. There are scores of them out there doing research in the physics of the upper atmosphere, geophysics, astrophysics and astronomy; there are weather satellites and communications satellites; there are technical satellites investigating the effects of space on paints, insulation, plastics, and metals; there are even spy satellites, although this is never admitted officially.

Some of them are energetically recording and transmitting data, others were stillborn and are orbiting in silence, some have outlived their usefulness but are still chattering away, cluttering up the wavebands, to the fury of the communications people, and some are dead of old age. For spacecraft are like living organisms; they're born, they live, they develop personalities and even eccentricities, and finally they die. However, Ed Habib, one of the resident geniuses in the Data Systems Division of the Goddard Space Flight Center, insists that satellites are like old soldiers. "They don't die. They just fade away."

I'm going to ignore the Manned Spacecraft program. It's been more than adequately covered by other writers, and anyway I belong to the Machine-in-Space school. Along with many other people I don't believe there's any real value in putting men into space, and if the Russians want to blow billions of rubles landing a cosmonaut on the moon, good luck to them. Our basketball team can still lick their basketball team. On the other hand I'm a devout believer in the value of the scientific satellite program which has never received the public attention it deserves.

So I'm going to write the behind-the-scenes biography of one family of satellites (there are many families), but it can't be a straightforward narrative, any more than the biography of a human family can be. I'll be forced to digress and go off on tangents to fill in the background and clarify the complex issues and conflicts involved, but we'll keep coming back to the mainstream of the story.

I'd like to start by plunging you into the middle of a family squabble. You may not understand it, but it will tune you in, so to speak, to the curious and colorful atmosphere of the satellite world. By the end of this biography you'll not only understand but will probably want to take sides.

2

Space Jargon

A CONFERENCE has been arranged in Building One at the Goddard Space Flight Center:

NATIONAL AERONAUTICS AND SPACE ADMINISTRATION
Goddard Space Flight Center
Greenbelt, Maryland 20771
OSO-II EXPERIMENTERS' MEETING
5 March 1965
Agenda

Observatory Status
Status of Data Reduction
Experiment Irregularities
Data Correlations Available
Experimenters' Experience
Analysis of Irregularities
Future OSO-II Operations

Building One is devoted to theoretical physics, and the conference room is at the head of a long corridor of offices which the irreverent have nicknamed Moon Hall. The offices are inhabited by mathematicians, and all the offices look alike; they contain untidy piles of journals and texts, blackboards covered with arcane equations, and sprawling youths staring into space.

You enter the conference room. It's crowded with thirty-odd scientists and engineers from the various institutions which are participating in this space mission. Very few of them resemble the shaggy scientists of stage and screen cliché; most of them look like bright young salesmen. They sit in double ranks around the long conference table. On one wall is the inevitable blackboard, as yet unblemished.

At the head of the table sits the chairman, Mr. Laurence Hogarth, the project manager of the mission. Hogarth is an Englishman. Behind Hogarth sits his partner, Dr. John Lindsay, the project scientist of the mission. Dr. Lindsay looks like a young Abe Lincoln. His feet are cocked up on a corner of the table. He is constantly relighting his pipe, and seems to be smoking matches.

The conference has been called to discuss the performance of a space satellite and the experiments on board. The discussion is quiet and businesslike, occasionally relieved by flashes of a scientist's idea of humor. Dr. Tousey from the Naval Research Laboratories is on his feet reporting the performance of his experiment. He is a gray-haired man with a modest manner.

"We're having difficulties with the Van Allen belt," Tousey says, not complaining. "We're getting too much noise. It may be from dust or snowflakes, the same that were photographed in rocket experiments three years ago. Also, the objective is fluorescing. We don't know why."

"Could it be from the sun?" Hogarth inquires.

"It couldn't be from the sun. We weren't locked on the

sun long enough. It might be from the Van Allen and Starfish radiation belts."

"What lens was used?"

Dr. Tousey glances at an assistant who answers the chairman. "I don't remember the glass number, but it was a special crown spectacle lens selected for minimum fluorescence."

"Have you correlated the fluorescent effect with the Van Allen belt?"

"We haven't reduced our data sufficiently to tell."

"Hmmm . . ." Hogarth meditates, then, "anything else?"

Dr. Tousey looks at his notes. "Yes, the spectroheliograph alignment is not perfect. It's off by three minutes in azimuth and four minutes in altitude. We have no idea why, except that the instrument may have been shaken up in the launch."

"I remember you had some trouble with the filter during tests," Lindsay drawls in a deep voice. "Did you leave it in?"

"Yes. Why?"

"I was wondering if it was shifted as a result of the centrifugal force of the spin-up, and that might account for it."

"It's an idea. You may be right."

The chairman waits for Dr. Tousey to continue. When it becomes apparent that this experimenter has nothing more to say, he calls on Dr. Hallam from the Goddard Space Flight Center. Dr. Hallam is a good-looking youngster, square-featured and sleek-haired. He speaks with maddening hesitation.

"Our photomultipliers . . . and counters . . . are . . . being saturated. . . . by . . . er . . . the Van Allen belt

. . . radiation . . . and . . . go . . . er . . . dead . . . at periods."

From the far end of the room, Professor Ed Ney, an astronomer from the University of Minnesota, chips in. He has a foggy voice and a buoyant manner. "I'm not having any trouble with my scintillation counter. It's rock-steady."

Hallam ignores this. With his eyes fixed on his notes he continues, "Another thing . . . We're getting . . . meaningless words . . . which have nothing . . . er . . . to do . . . with the . . . experiment."

One of his assistants adds briskly, "On one orbit we got five readouts of sixty-three."

Lindsay rumbles, "Does anyone else use sixty-three in his experiment?"

There is a burst of laughter. Lindsay relights his pipe and squints at the flame. "Has anybody looked at an all-channel print-out of the first ten orbits?"

Nobody has, and evidently nobody understands why the question was asked. Lindsay explains, "What I had in mind was the possibility of the attitude of the experiment in the Van Allen belt being responsible for data difficulties . . . That is, the electromagnetic field in one particular position might do it."

Professor Ed Ney suggests, "Also hot spots in the Van Allen belt might be the cause, but I'm not having that trouble."

Without looking at Ney, Lindsay drawls, "The only conclusion I can make is that Ed's experiment isn't working. He doesn't see the Van Allen belt. He doesn't get any noise. He just gets results."

In the laughter that follows, Ney bounces to his feet. "Everything's working fine, except that we're playing a kind of space roulette. There's always a chance that the satellite sail will obscure our telescope. You can spot these events in the data readout, and the average is normal, about one in five." He looks around and grins. "You guys ought to quit trying to do these hard experiments that are significant. You ought to do the ones that don't mean a damn thing, but are easy."

Another burst of laughter and Ney sits down. The chairman draws a deep breath and turns to Dr. Reeves from the Harvard College Observatory. This is an unhappy moment. The Harvard experiment, an attempt to measure solar energy in the ultraviolet spectrum, was one of the most important aboard the satellite, for political as well as scientific reasons, and it failed, "crapped out," the engineers say.

Dr. Reeves is a slender young man with a narrow face. "This is our best guess," he reports gloomily. "We had an arc, a short-duration pulse, that blew the electronics."

"What makes you think you had an arc?" Lindsay demands.

"We had high-count readings immediately on turn-on, which died away." Reeves hesitates. "Rather than arc you can call it a high-voltage breakdown."

Hogarth takes over the discussion. "But you must have an atmosphere for the discharge."

"Yes."

"Where do you think the arc took place?"

"In or near the photomultiplier."

"What would make a photomultiplier arc?"

In a flat voice Reeves itemizes, "Gas pressure. Contamination of dust or material. Ions inside the box."

Hogarth thinks for a moment. "Was the equipment potted?"

"No."

"Was the cabling open?" Hogarth's tone suggests disapproval.

"At three points. It was all insulated, but it was unshielded at three places."

"Could you diagram the circuitry for us?"

One of Dr. Reeves's assistants gets up, goes to the blackboard, and chalks the circuitry of the Harvard experiment in formal electronic symbols. His exposition takes ten minutes.

After absorbing this, the chairman asks, "How much testing did it get?"

"All the tests, including the Terminal-3 test at the Cape." Dr. Reeves sounds slightly defensive. "It never arced in the tests. It was thermal-vacuum tested and accepted, and shake-tested and accepted."

Lindsay drawls, "Was there any material used on the terminals that might have whiskered?"

"No. We used a number of materials. They were all silver-soldered. None of them was likely to whisker."

"Soldering is always the crucial problem," Hogarth mutters. He pronounces it the English way, "sollderring."

Dr. Reeves consults his notes. "There might have been a mechanical failure; a wire shaken loose and crossed. Or, since the photomultiplier is magnetic, a bit of metal filing might have been shaken loose by the launch and been attracted to it. There might have been ions or electrons inside the box where they caused the high voltage to arc. There might have been a photoelectric yield from the metals, an emission resulting from exposure to sunlight."

"But would the buildup of magnetic and dielectric dust

particles on a terminal be enough to create an arc?" Lindsay asks.

"Yes." Reeves nods sadly. "It only has to happen once, and then a carbon path is established."

Hogarth attempts to dispel the gloom by adjourning the conference for lunch with an administrative joke. "We'll meet again at one o'clock sharp, gentlemen. Try to be back by one-thirty."

In the building cafeteria you pick up snatches of shop talk from the experimenters and engineers:

"They were demonstrating particle acceleration in the lab to some visitors. They set up a cloud chamber so the visitors could see the particles emerging visually. They'd been walking back and forth in front of the source without thinking about it, but as soon as they saw the particles ramming through the cloud chamber they began ducking and dodging."

"I hear you're in luck; you've got an extra three microseconds."

"Four. Isn't it great!"

"One of the toughest problems was reflected light from the oceans. It was blinding the photomultiplier tubes; they were going snow-blind. They had to hang a sensor outside the satellite to shut off the photomultiplier tubes every time the oceans began shining up into them."

"This congressman was pestering me about why a satellite won't last three years in space. I think he felt he wasn't getting his money's worth. Finally I said to him, 'Look, a TV set has two hundred electronic parts. A satellite has thirty-five thousand electronic parts. And a TV set doesn't hold up too damn well in your own living room.' "

"Ames Research has come up with a wild theory about Martian atmosphere. They say if the atmosphere is nitrogen and carbon dioxide, then if it's exposed to ultraviolet radiation the combination will produce sugar which might be sifting down constantly. Manna from heaven."

Ed Ney is entertaining one table with his plans for an eclipse expedition to Tahiti aboard a schooner yacht loaned to the expedition by a rich playboy. Then he describes the near-fatal goof he pulled in his own experiment on the satellite, and the miracle that saved him.

Ney had a telescope mounted on the spacecraft to investigate zodiacal light and the mysterious airglow layer that mantles the earth. He had neglected to calibrate the time-lapse between the sensing of the phenomena by his telescope and the transmission of the data back to earth. He received information, but never knew how much time it took to arrive; which meant that he never knew the exact moment when the reported event took place.

"Then we had a lucky break," Ney said. "Our telescope picked up a tremendous thunderstorm with lightning discharges on one of the passes over the nightside of the earth. We were able to measure the time-lapse between the storm and the reception of the data on it, and that enabled us to calibrate all our other results." He grinned. "When those Harvard guys were boasting about their discharge, I wanted to tell them about our electric storm. That was the biggest discharge of all."

This is a sample of space from the inside; unintelligible to you now, of course, but soon to be easily understood, I hope. The problem of understanding our space program is merely one of simplifying the complexities of its mechanics, and translating the perplexities of its language.

Its mechanics seem mysterious to the layman, but only because he rarely has the opportunity to familiarize himself with complex machinery. Bob Mattingly, one of the NASA engineers, points out that today most machinery is concealed inside covers, and suggests that the most complicated naked machine the average man has a chance to inspect is a can opener or an eggbeater. Yet each of the details that add up to a spacecraft is no more complicated than an eggbeater. One of the most brilliant devices designed for OGO, the Orbiting Geophysical Observatory, was based on the level-wind fishing reel.

Terminology is the second barrier. The Space Age, like the Computer Age and the Transistor Age, has been forced to invent its own language with a special vocabulary that defies deduction. Wives ask their husbands the difference between a satellite and a probe, and the gentlemen are often at a loss. President Johnson, referring to the Mariner Mars mission in his State of the Union address, spoke proudly of "a rocket on its way to Mars," and spacemen across the country rolled their eyes to heaven in anguish. "The *rocket*'s under three miles of water in the South Atlantic," they grumbled.

The introductory step, then, is to clear away confusion with a simple description of spacecraft and what they do. The generic name for all objects launched into space is spacecraft. Spacecraft may be roughly divided into satellites and probes. Satellites are craft which are launched into an orbit around the earth. Probes are craft which are launched into space beyond the earth. Neither satellites nor probes are rockets.

Rockets are vehicles. They carry a payload . . . a satellite or a probe . . . to some place, but not necessarily all the way to the place where the payload is going. In essence, what they do is start the payload on its way with a healthy shove. Wives and Presidents are confused by the fact that military rockets carry a payload of explosives, and both vehicle and payload arrive at the target together. There's no need to separate them when the whole shebang is going to blow up.

But vehicle and payload need not be permanently bound together. Some of the Army long-range missiles are step rockets built in stages, and only the warhead arrives at the target. Sounding rockets carry a light payload of instruments into the upper atmosphere, are detached, and fall back to earth. Momentum carries the payload up a little higher, and then it parachutes down for recovery.

The giant Delta, Agena, Centaur, and Saturn rockets are the vehicles that lift the heavy payloads up into space. These are step rockets, too; built in stages. The first stage, or booster, pushes the payload up above the atmosphere. Then it's detached and drops back to earth. The second and third stages ignite and burn in succession, and add enough additional thrust to insert the payload into orbit or trajectory. Then they, too, are detached and fall back to earth.

Sometimes there is only a second stage which is ignited and burns twice. Sometimes the final stage acquires enough velocity to achieve orbit itself, and circles the earth many times before its orbit decays and it drops. The important thing to remember is that only the payload remains in space. Sooner or later, the vehicles end up somewhere at the bottom of the ocean.

Many people are under the impression that launching a

spacecraft is similar to shooting a gun; you take aim, fire, and there goes the payload on its prescribed course. It's much more similar to a tennis serve. You loft the ball into the air. That's the boost with the first or first and second stages. The ball reaches the top of the toss and hangs for a moment before starting to drop. Engineers call this the Parking Orbit or the Coasting Orbit. At that moment the tennis racket hits the ball and drives it toward the opponent's court. This is the ignition and thrust of the final stage which inserts the payload into trajectory.

All orbits around the earth are elliptical. Think of the earth's gravitational attraction as an elastic leash; it holds on to the spacecraft but stretches and contracts. Some orbits are long and narrow, others are nearly circular; it all depends on the purpose of the satellite, on the particular regions of space to be surveyed. For trajectory men the circle is merely a special form of an ellipse. They call it a degenerate ellipse, which sounds unkind.

Space probes fly trajectories that are elliptical, too. For example, the Ranger Moon probes, held by the elastic leash of the earth's gravity, would have swung around somewhere beyond the moon's orbit and returned if the target itself had not blocked the path. The Mariner Mars probe also flew an elliptical trajectory. In this case, however, the spacecraft traveled so far from the earth that it slipped its leash and became the subject of the sun's massive attraction. Now it's in a class with the asteroids revolving around the sun. In other words, after it passed Mars in the encounter it did not continue on out into deep space, but swung back in a heliocentric orbit.

There is another type of small rocket engine added to deep space probes. It is built into the spacecraft, cannot be detached, and is used for the mid-course maneuver which is easily understood if we return to the firearms analogy. You can't achieve perfect aim with the boost and later stage rockets when you're shooting at a target as small as a seventy-five-mile crater on the moon, or as distant as an encounter with Mars three hundred fifty million miles away, for the same reason that a revolver is not as accurate as a rifle.

The rocket vehicles combine to make a powerful revolver, but with a barrel too short to allow long-range precision. All they can do is launch you in the general direction in which you want to go. Then the craft must be tracked along its trajectory until the inaccuracy of its aim is known. It's corrected by igniting the built-in rocket engine and altering the course. This midcourse maneuver has the effect of lengthening the gun barrel.

The sophisticated complexities of orbits and trajectories, tracking and data retrieval, test and evaluation of spacecraft, research and development, and the design of experiments will be discussed later. The important thing now is to realize that there are no mathematical or engineering terrors involved. When the special space language is translated into everyday speech, everything can be simply explained and easily understood.

One more language difficulty should be mentioned; abbreviations. Governments and institutions have a weakness for long, pompous titles which no man in his right mind would ever use in casual conversation. For example, Cal Tech insists that the title *The Jet Propulsion Laboratory of the California Institute of Technology* be used in all publications. Spacemen won't stand for this sort of nonsense and refer to it as JPL. More of their shorthand follows:

NASA (pronounced "Naa-suh") is, as you probably know, the National Aeronautics and Space Administration. NRL stands for the Naval Research Laboratory, one of the most powerful and influential research centers in the armed forces. DOD (pronounced "D.O.D.") is the Department of Defense. Goddard is the Goddard Space Flight Center in Greenbelt, Maryland, the coordinating center for all space sciences. Huntsville and Marshall are short for the von Braun rocketry group at the George C. Marshall Space Flight Center in Huntsville, Alabama. R&D stands for Research and Development, a constantly recurring theme in the space program. BBRC are the initials of the Ball Brothers Research Corporation, one of NASA's most important private contractors. There are others in common use which I'll translate as we go along.

If I seem to be insulting your intelligence by explaining obvious things like how to pronounce NASA, it's because one never knows how much knowledge to take for granted. Dr. Jim Kupperian of the astrophysics department at Goddard tells a story about the San Francisco Fair where they were exhibiting an orrery, which is a clockwork model of the solar system. You can usually see one in a planetarium.

"The French consul came on a visit. He was distinguished, elegant, and sophisticated. He had an American interpreter along to help explain the exhibits to him. The consul stopped at the orrery and was very much interested. He asked dozens of questions in French, which the interpreter answered, and became extremely excited. The interpreter turned around and said, 'We're in trouble now. This guy just found out that the earth goes around the sun.' "

3

Men and Satellites

SPUTNIK went into orbit and the United States went into shock. It was the best thing that could have happened to us. We had always claimed that we were the most advanced nation in the world, technologically speaking, and the world believed us. The neutral countries were sending a majority of their engineering students to study in the United States, and only a small number to the USSR. Then the Russians broke into space, and the proportion began to reverse.

The Russian achievement forced us to put up or shut up. Spacemen in America deplore the attitudes in both countries that have turned scientific research into a propaganda vehicle. Space is the most hostile environment ever encountered by man, and spacemen around the world feel like brothers in arms. Politicians may turn space programs into national rivalries, but the American spacemen applaud the Russian victories over the common enemy, and hope the Russian spacemen react the same way to our successes.

Yet they are forced to admit that without this political rivalry our space program would still be a mere scientific curiosity. Dr. William Pickering, director of JPL, Cal Tech's Jet Propulsion Laboratory, said, "I'm thinking what would have happened in the IGY [the International Geophysical Year] if we'd put up a satellite and the Russians had not. What would be happening now? Probably we'd just be playing around with a few satellites."

Instead, our space program turned into a gigantic enterprise. In 1958 Congress passed the National Aeronautics and Space Act that established NASA, and allocated an astronomical budget to it. NASA invited Cal Tech's JPL and von Braun's rocketry group in Huntsville, Alabama to join the organization, and began setting up the Goddard Space Flight Center in Greenbelt, Maryland, the Manned Spacecraft Center in Houston, Texas, the Institute for Space Studies in New York City, and many others.

To staff the organization, NASA made a raid on the scientific community that left scars which have not yet healed, and the program itself put the oddest combinations of men into harness together. One of the strangest was the team of Lindsay and Hogarth. Both are interesting examples of the type of men who are a part of our space program. Both played vital and tragic roles in the life history of the Orbiting Solar Observatory which eventually proved to be one of the most hazardous and deadly missions in NASA's program.

Laurence Hogarth (called "Hoge," and sometimes "Father Laurence") is in his early fifties. He's slight, trim, silver-haired, and wears the cropped moustache typical of the English civil servant. His courteous reserve is also typically English, and a source of confusion to many Americans who think him rude and snobbish. Like most educated Englishmen, he speaks in full, well-rounded sentences. Some of his colleagues, accustomed to the casual telegraphese we speak in America, think him affected.

Hogarth was born in Cardiff of a well-to-do English family, and says he always felt like an alien being raised in Wales. He says he's only remotely related to the great eighteenth-century English artist William Hogarth. He received a conventional upper-class schooling until the depression of the thirties set in. "We had the depression in England too, you know, so I took off, aged sixteen, and won a scholarship at London University where I took a B.S. in chemistry."

He showed a marked capacity for mechanical engineering but had no patience for the study. "Anyone can pick up engineering, but you can't pick up chemistry, so I did graduate work in chemistry, specializing in the electronic basis of organic reactions. I've always been angry with myself for being too impatient to take a rather easy Ph.D." He's right to feel that way. Today the passport to promotion is a doctorate.

In 1937 Hogarth went into the British War Office as an expert in industrial chemistry. His job was supervising the construction of plants manufacturing chemicals and explosives to make sure they would follow the procedures necessary for the production of quality products. "I was forced to scrap with large industries to get things done right, and I won. I would have been fired in the States for fighting with Du Pont; over there I was promoted, concealed, and given extra leave to get me out of the way for a while. But I got the reputation for being keen but restless."

In 1940, aged twenty-eight, he was sent to Canada to check the installations of munitions manufacturers, and then posted to New York as consultant for the British Purchasing Commission, again supervising the procedures of English-owned munitions plants. "Munitions manufacture was a forgotten art in the forties. It hadn't been practiced since the end of World War I. No one realized how carefully and precisely they had to be made."

When Lend-Lease began, the English-owned plants were immediately turned over to the United States, but Hogarth stayed on as a munitions expert supervising the specifications of the war materiel shipped overseas to the United Kingdom. When the early attempts were made to design and build guided missiles, Hogarth was brought in as an explosives expert, and in 1947 was asked to remain in the States as a consultant for the Navy.

"I became associate director of R&D [Research and Development] at a Navy arsenal, but I had to leave in 1953 because I'd made the place too hot for me. In fact, I ran my department, and that was the trouble." He admits that he still has a tendency to be abrupt with people whom he considers fools, even if they happen to be admirals. He's resigned to the fact that this impatience will probably prevent his rising very high in the NASA organization.

Money was becoming increasingly important to him. Government salaries are small; he'd seen fortunes made during the war; he was married and had a son to educate. Hogarth scraped together what money he had saved and attempted to get into the wholesale drug business. After some promising negotiations for the purchase of a small pharmaceutical firm, the deal collapsed, and Hogarth was left high and dry. When this happened he went back into government service at an Army arsenal, and then was invited to join the ballistics research laboratory at Aberdeen. He joined NASA in 1960 as a project manager, and was teamed up with John Lindsay.

No one more dissimilar to Hogarth could have been found. Dr. John Lindsay was forty-two, tall, raw-boned, dark-complexioned, and poker-faced. Where Hogarth was suave and trim, Lindsay was country-boy; rugged and ugly-attractive. Hogarth's secretary served him morning and afternoon tea on a chaste tray. Lindsay was constantly ambling out to his secretary's percolator to pour himself a cup of black coffee. Where Hogarth managed people with carefully planned and staged strategy, Lindsay overawed people with his intent concentration and the rumble of his deep Southern voice. In a quiet way his attractive personality was overpowering.

In one way the men were very similar. They were both under a severe strain because of the extremely high stakes of the space program, and each had a characteristic foible which betrayed the strain. Hogarth carried an amber bead in his pocket, and when the stress became too strong for him, would take it out and finger it nervously. Lindsay used his pipe in the same way, constantly relighting it when he was under duress.

Lindsay was born and raised in Bedford, Virginia. Like Hogarth, he suffered badly from the depression. His father was a real estate broker who was practically wiped out in the thirties. As a boy, Lindsay was interested in radio and electronics, and said that he and some friends contrived to build microscopes and telescopes. Asked if he had ground his own telescope lenses, he drawled, "No, we sort of swiped what we needed."

Lindsay finished high school in 1934, but there was no

money in the family so he went to work for a couple of years. Then he entered Guilford College, a small Quaker school in North Carolina, to which his father and grandfather had gone. He had no idea of what he wanted to do, but science was his best subject, and he majored in physics and math. "I graduated in 1940, and I had a hell of a time trying to get a good job for four or five years. I worked as an electrician in a shipyard. The gantry elevators down at the Cape remind me of the elevators we used when we worked on the ships."

In 1945 Lindsay got a job with the Raytheon Company as an electronics engineer working on Planned Position Indicators and other radar devices, but when the Navy canceled the war contracts he was fired. He went back to his hometown and struggled. He'd saved a little money. He got married. He taught math, chemistry, and physics at the local high school. He worked on real estate deals with his father part time.

He was powerfully motivated by an admirable but tormenting ambition to win recognition in science and leave his mark on history, and had never taken his sights off a doctorate. In 1947 he went to the University of North Carolina at Chapel Hill for his master's degree in physics, and then taught for a year at Virginia Polytechnic. "But I'd worked with a professor from NRL [the Naval Research Laboratory] at Chapel Hill, and he got a grant to do some research on ballistics. He asked me to come back and work with him on the project and continue my graduate work. I finally got my Ph.D. in 1953.

"Then I applied for jobs at several plants, and would you believe it, I was accepted at all of them." His poker face betrayed no amazement. "For the first time in my life I felt

I was starting to get the breaks. I went with Du Pont to do research in applied physics, but I didn't like it much. I wasn't permitted to work in the areas I was interested in." His attention had finally focused on solar physics.

Some of Lindsay's friends from Chapel Hill were at NRL, and they talked John into joining the laboratory in 1956. Lindsay immediately plunged into the problems of upper atmosphere research with rockets. "But there are a lot of experiments which a rocket can't do. Solar flares, for instance." (Solar flares are sudden brilliant eruptions, associated with sunspots, which flood the earth with high-energy particles, often disrupting radio and television communications. They don't occur very often, and rarely last longer than an hour.)

"One time in California," Lindsay went on, "we sat for two weeks with our rockets, waiting for a flare. There wasn't anything. We had a direct line to the Mt. Wilson observatory, so we called them up one Friday and asked if there was any chance of a flare over the weekend. They told us nothing doing, so we all went into L.A. for the weekend to live it up a little. Wouldn't you know, that Sunday was one of the biggest flares in the sun's history. But even if we'd been there, the rockets wouldn't have been too good. Suppose you do have a flare and you're ready for it? You're always late. You never observe the beginning."

He was wondering how to cope with the inadequacies of rocket research when he was asked to join the newly formed NASA. He was reluctant to accept the offer. "I'd read the NASA act and liked it, it was all-inclusive; but the NRL group had had an understanding that we'd all stick together at NRL, and I didn't want to break that. Then Homer Newell [NASA's administrator of Space Science and Applications] transferred from NRL to NASA, a few others shifted over, too, and that broke up the group. So I joined.

"I came over to NASA expecting to head up the solar physics group at the Goddard Space Flight Center, but Goddard didn't even exist yet. NASA was quite small then. All they had was JPL. NASA headquarters had a hundred people in it at the most. Everyone was doing more than they possibly could. Morale was high. Things got done quickly because it wasn't turned into an organization. It was tight-knit."

In fact, this small, tightly knit fraternity already contained the seeds of its own destruction. In its anxiety to get the space program off the ground, NASA had begun by inviting Dr. Harry Goett to become director of the new Goddard Space Flight Center and put it together. Goett was an engineer, a man of fierce independence and complete self-reliance. It was understood that he was to be given a free hand to get Goddard built, staffed, and started on its program of science in space. Goett was a maverick, and so was Lindsay. They became close friends, and when the inevitable clash with the management types came, they found it impossible to make concessions. They fought and lost together.

Congress had given NASA money for fiscal 1958, and the money was available for implementing missions. Lindsay began work as a project scientist in early 1959. I've used the expressions project manager and project scientist. They're best explained with a digression on the way a space mission comes into being; in other words, how a family of satellites is born. We'll return to Hogarth and Lindsay very shortly.

Almost everybody is interested in the beginnings of things, but sometimes it's difficult for experts to answer questions about beginnings because they're too close to their work to be able to understand the layman's ignorance. I remember spending an entire day badgering the IBM engineers, trying to get an answer to the simple question "How do you start a computer on a problem; what's the first thing you do?" I was thinking in terms of starting a car by turning on the ignition, and I couldn't understand why they didn't seem to be able to explain. Much later it finally came out that you don't start computers; they're always turned on. Fortunately the start of a space mission can be simply and directly described.

The Steering Committee of NASA, which is made up of leading scientists, begins everything with long-range programming, looking ahead from ten to twenty years, and planning what experiments should be done. Experiment is the term used to describe any investigation of phenomena, and also the apparatus used for the investigation. If you send up a Geiger counter to record high-energy particles, that's an experiment. Sometimes the experimental apparatus is called the "package."

The Steering Committee asks: What do we want to be doing by way of experiments when sunspot activity reaches a maximum? What should be investigated at the next favorable conjunction of the earth and Mars? What are the steps to be taken in preparation for a soft landing on the moon? What technological satellites should be launched for experiments in control systems, communications, radiation damage, and thermal erosion? In addition to this there's short-range planning in terms of how many and what type spacecraft were launched last year, and how many NASA should plan on launching next year.

When the Steering Committee has decided on the types and purposes of the satellites for future launching, each mission is turned over to a partnership of project manager and project scientist. The project manager is the engineering supervisor. It's his job to get the satellite built, tested, and passed, and to make sure the various experiments on board are also properly constructed and tested. He must see to it that everybody concerned is working on schedule. Above all else, he alone is responsible for the success of the mission as a whole.

The role of the project scientist is purely scientific as opposed to the engineering aspects of the mission. He is in charge of whatever experiments NASA may be flying on the satellite, and he may or may not be an experimenter himself. In addition, he acts as liaison between the experimental scientists and the engineers who are building the satellite. There is a constant danger of antipathy between the engineers and scientists, and communications sometimes break down. Bob Baumann, chief of Spacecraft Integration at Goddard, was asked, "Do you have any basic mechanism in spacecraft that always gives you trouble?" He grunted, "Only the scientists."

But Hogarth, also representing the engineer's point of view, said, "It wouldn't be fair to give the impression that we're at loggerheads all the time with scientists. We're really not. There *are* a few we'd never fly again, but on the whole they're extremely good and realistic.

"One reason for this class warfare is the fact that most of the money is spent on the engineering aspects of satellites, and the scientists bitterly resent it. Another of the difficulties with the NASA scientists is that sometimes they're not the top men in their field, so they haven't been able to get into the faculty of their choice. They go to work for the government and feel like they're slumming. They're nice chaps, but they want to get something out of it, so they take the attitude 'You can't push *me* around.' "

Supporting the project manager and the project scientist are a business representative responsible for funding, contracting, personnel, and so forth, Tracking and Data Retrieval representatives, and Test and Evaluation representatives. These are the men who make up the mission team, and they command all the resources of the particular NASA center in which they're working.

Under the direction of the project manager and project scientist, plans and specifications of the proposed satellite are drafted, and a complete description written up giving the purpose, orbit, weight, dimensions, power supply, transmission systems, tracking stations, launch facilities, probable life of the satellite, and the schedule deadlines that must be met. Plans for the proposed satellites are printed in a Blue Book. Here, for example, are the contents of the Blue Book for December, 1963:

Biosatellite Program
Tiros, Tiros Wheel, and Nimbus Spacecraft
X-15A2 Research Airplane
Sounding Rocket Program
Orbiting Geophysical Observatory (OGO)
Orbiting Solar Observatory (OSO)
Advanced Orbiting Solar Observatory (AOSO)
International Satellite for Ionosphere Studies (ISIS)
Orbiting Astronomical Observatory (OAO)
Pioneer Spacecraft
Anchored Interplanetary Explorer (AIMP)

The point is that while NASA flies its own experiments on the satellite, it also makes sure to provide extra space for other experimenters. The Blue Books are issued semiannually and sent to all universities, laboratories, and institutions which might be interested in participating in one of the missions with a package of their own, which NASA finances.

Proposals are submitted by experimenters and are judged by special subcommittees. The proposals are categorized into one of four classes: 1. Good experiment, first-class scientist, go at once. 2. For various reasons (package too bulky, demands too much power, incompatible with other experiments) give this second priority. 3. Good idea but needs further testing. 4. Rejection, usually for one of two reasons; either technically it's a good experiment but its proposer doesn't know what to do with it, or the entire experiment is technologically unsound. It has happened that the same proposal, submitted to two different subcommittees, has been placed in Class 1 by one committee and in Class 4 by the other, which made faces very red indeed.

There aren't many proposals submitted; around fifteen per small spacecraft which can carry no more than six experiments, and fifty to sixty for the larger craft carrying twenty experiments or more. Very often parallel experiments are submitted, and occasionally downright crackpot experiments are proposed. The prospective participants are sometimes asked to come before the subcommittee and make a case for their proposals. The arguments can get pretty hot, but very few of the applicants go away sore, provided they're given an explanation of why they were turned down.

The subcommittees then send their recommendations to the Program office which integrates the various experiments and sometimes shuffles them from satellite to satellite, but only with the technical concurrence as to feasibility of the project managers, the project scientists, and the experimenters. Then it sends the program back up to the Steering Committee which votes on whether to go ahead with it. The Steering Committee is the final judge of payloads, but it usually accepts the recommendations of the subcommittees. All this is prenatal development. The mission is born at the moment that NASA signs a piece of paper saying so. The satellite, of course, isn't born until the moment it flies.

Now everything goes into high gear. The project manager lets contracts for the construction of the satellite, sets up working schedules, and begins hounding everybody to stick to them. And now the fur begins to fly.

4

The Creation of OSO

Lindsay came to NASA in late 1958 with an idea. Since the sounding rockets were inadequate for solar research, he wanted to put a solar observatory into orbit, and he began talking up his proposal. He says, "NASA, in the spring of 1959, was in its planning stage. Most of the big projects were conceived then. We were all working hard and these were spare-time sessions, not committee meetings. We were all scientists and we sat around with our feet on the table and talked."

Lindsay was working on the Thor-Able program which NASA had taken over from the Air Force. This had been an attempt to put a spacecraft into a lunar orbit and it had failed. Lindsay took on the unfinished business of Able 3 and Able 4. Able 3 was to be launched into a highly elliptical orbit around the earth. Two Able 4's were to be launched, one on an orbit around the moon, the other on a mission to Venus.

"Able 3 was launched in August, 1959," Lindsay said, "and was a raving success by the standards of those days.

The data recovery was good, and the scientists were happy."

To give you some idea of the standards of 1959, here is the performance of Able 3, renamed Explorer VI after it was flown. (NASA's practice is to give spacecraft a working title while they're in construction, and a public name after they're flown.) Explorer VI flew an orbit that was 156 miles from the earth at its closest, and 27,357 miles from earth at its farthest. It carried eight experiments measuring the levels of the earth's radiation belts, scanning the earth's cloud cover, mapping the earth's magnetic field, counting micrometeorites, and studying the behavior of radio waves. It lived for two months.

The lunar mission was a fiasco. Hogarth, who had joined NASA by then and had been teamed with Lindsay on the rest of the Able project, said, "We got the go-ahead on the lunar orbiter in February, 1960, and flew it in September. The vehicle failed. We cranked up another one and flew it in December, and the vehicle failed again.

"It was a three-stage job; an Atlas booster with two upper stages. We monitored the upper stages but hadn't the time or the staff to monitor the Atlas, so we were forced to take the booster for granted. All the stages as delivered were capable of functioning. I'm convinced that it was an interstage failure both times, but this has never been established by the rocketry people." This interstage failure was to come back and haunt Hogarth five years later.

The Venus probe had to be changed to a deep-space probe because Venus was on the far side of the sun, and was launched in March, 1960. Lindsay said, "It went very well. It was the deepest shot so far. They communicated with it out to twenty-five million miles. (The Mariner IV Mars probe of 1965 communicated from a distance of 191 million miles.) The experiments went well. This was the first look at interplanetary space."

The Venus probe was renamed Pioneer V after it was flown. It was launched on a trajectory around the sun which came within seventy-five million miles of the sun at its closest, and went out to ninety-two million miles from the sun at its farthest. It carried four experiments testing long-range radio communications, and measuring high-energy particles, solar flare effects, and magnetic field phenomena. It stayed in communication with the earth for three months before moving out of range.

During all this activity Lindsay was still selling his hope for an orbiting solar observatory. Hogarth described him in action at the time. "He's a Scot. He's honest and speaks his mind. He's a canny in-fighter, a courthouse-steps politician who knows how to get things done, which is unusual for a scientist. He reacts very hard to the smallest opposition. He's a loner, and so am I, so it's very difficult to kill both of us in one fight. John never lets his right hand know what his left hand is doing. This is how he's able to ride off opposition.

"The trouble with John was that he always wanted to fly his own experiments, which created suspicion on the part of the other participants. They were afraid they wouldn't get a fair deal. There's nobody as good as John at looking at an experiment and telling whether or not it will work, but he won't do this. He's not interested in any experiments outside his own. He doesn't want to be a civil servant; he wants to be a great research scientist.

"Another of his difficulties was the NRL/NASA syndrome. There's a funny feeling of awkwardness and tension between the people who left NRL for NASA, and those who remained with NRL. NRL didn't like John for the reason that he left them for NASA."

But the main difficulty standing in Lindsay's way was the fact that his idea of an orbiting solar observatory required a spacecraft that would always point at the sun while it revolved around the earth, and the NASA people weren't at all sure that this could be done. They asked industry for advice. The Perkin-Elmer Company suggested building an inertial wheel into the satellite which would act as a sort of gyroscopic compass to keep the craft pointed at the sun. It was a good idea, which is now being used in the Orbiting Astronomical Observatory, but back in 1960 it would have been too expensive and taken too long to build.

One aircraft armament company suggested using a spinning satellite with a bullet belt or bandolier of cartridges around its circumference. The satellite would point at the sun, and if it got out of line, its aim could be corrected by firing appropriate shots from the belt. Lindsay said, "We decided we didn't think much of that."

What Lindsay had in mind for his satellite was a pointing control that he'd used with success in his sounding rockets when he was with NRL. It was manufactured by, of all people, the Ball Brothers company. Ball Brothers is known in every American kitchen as the maker of Mason jars. Their pointing control is the heart and soul of almost every modern satellite and space probe, and has a colorful history.

Ball Brothers is one of the largest and wealthiest privately owned companies in the world. One of their forward-looking policies is to retain an agent whose sole function is to locate promising properties for them to acquire. After World War II he found a company in Boulder, Colorado, which had patented a new load-cell device for weighing loaded trucks. He suggested that Ball Brothers take over.

Ball Brothers bought the company but discovered that the load-cell system had a bad design. Boulder is the home of the University of Colorado, so they called in David Stacey, a design consultant, from the science faculty to solve the problem. Stacey investigated and advised Ball Brothers to abandon the load cell; the basic design was bad and could not be salvaged. Then the question arose of what to do with the plant in Boulder. They asked Stacey's advice.

Stacey also happened to be a specialist in upper-atmosphere research. He told them that he and some colleagues at the University had been developing a rocket-pointing control for the Air Force Aerobee-Hi rocket. He suggested that if Ball Brothers wanted to go into the space business they might take over. The company hired Stacey and all the experts at the University who had worked on the device, set up the Ball Brothers Research Corporation, and went into business making pointing controls for Army and Air Force rockets in the early 1950's.

The control is based on two simple appliances which had been around for a long time; the servomotor and the light sensor. The servomotor has an automatic control to prevent its overshooting the mark by any significant amount. The principle is similar to the trick used in making a turn with an automobile. You swing the steering wheel to the right, the car turns right, but before it has completed its turn you're already easing the wheel back to the left so that the car will be moving in a straight line at the finish of the turn. The first servomechanism was a steam-operated ship's rudder, invented in 1868. As the rudder approached the desired position, the steam valve automatically began closing down, so that by the time the rudder reached its specified position, the steam pressure was off.

The light sensor is a silicon cell which has the property of developing a charge of voltage or current whenever light strikes it. The amount of current developed depends on the intensity of the light. All of us are familiar with the light sensor. In a very simple form it's the basis of the automatic door, and has been in use for many years. When your body blocks the beam of light shining across the entrance to a door, the sensor that has been receiving the beam reacts to the light change, and the door opens automatically.

The purpose of the pointing control is to aim a craft at a light source and keep it pointed at that source. In the case of the early sounding rockets it was used to keep the rockets locked on the sun. Its operation was quite simple. "Eyes" are mounted on opposite sides of the rocket. The eyes consist of ordinary lenses which focus the image of the sun on silicon solar cells, which then develop a current. If the rocket is not pointed directly at the sun, this means that one eye will receive more light than the other, and consequently its silicon solar cell will develop a larger voltage than the other.

The cells are linked to a servomotor which, in turn, is linked to the rocket flight controls. Now if the right eye develops more current than the left, the servomotor responds by tilting the rocket down to the right. This turns the right eye away from the sun, and brings the left eye up toward the sun. If now the left eye is developing more current than the right, the controls tilt the rocket back to the left. The servomotor will not overshoot the mark by much, so this canting from side to side continues in smaller and smaller arcs until at last both sensors are producing equal currents, which means that the rocket is at last pointed directly at the sun. Then the servomotor is cut off.

This was the pointing control in its early form (today it's far more sophisticated), and at the time it was a marvelous machine. It gave a high performance, and above all else it was incredibly simple; it had a minimum of internal complications. As Fred Dolder, one of the Ball Brothers directors at Boulder, says, "It was a gutless wonder."

But the problem was whether it could be adapted for use in a satellite which had severe power constraints. A sounding rocket supplies three hundred watts of electric power which is used for no more than five minutes, and this is ample for operating servosystems. A satellite could provide six watts of power at the most, and that had to be available for twelve months. Ball Brothers was asked if they could make the transition.

The company was positive they could. They drew up a proposal for NASA and pointed out that time was in the satellite's favor. Instead of being forced to acquire the sun in a few seconds, it could take minutes to do the job. Also, they didn't have to contend with the basic imbalance of a rocket. Trying to keep a rocket on course is like trying to balance a broom, handle-end up. A satellite could be balanced so perfectly that the servomotor wouldn't have to do heavy work. Both these factors meant a tremendous saving in power requirements.

However, there still was strong opposition to the satellite at NASA. Lindsay said, "We had a lot of critics. We violated engineering rules . . . they thought. You can't have moving parts in a vacuum. You can't use DC motors because of the lubrication problems. We had to plan on using slip rings, and slip rings are frowned on for use even on earth because they wear out. Most people thought it was a noble experiment that wouldn't work."

Ball Brothers didn't help the cause any when they estimated that the cost of developing a satellite-pointing control would be three hundred thousand dollars. Nevertheless, Lindsay fought, argued, persuaded, and politicked, and finally got the official go-ahead through what he called, "a sort of bootleg operation." Looking back at the debate today, one Ball Brothers executive says, "The whole thing wasn't planned; it just happened." True, but Lindsay made it happen.

Two orbiting solar observatories were scheduled and numbered S-16 and S-17. When satellites are planned they're given numbers and lettered "S" for scientific research, and "A" for applications such as weather and communications. As I mentioned before, they're renamed after they're flown, but in this case S-16 and S-17 were merely called OSO, pronounced "Oh-so." A third satellite was started several years later as a backup or replacement for the other two in case anything went wrong, and was numbered S-57.

S-16 and S-17 were first planned in early 1959, and they should be placed in perspective with a cross-section of some of the other NASA projects at the time. At the Jet Propulsion Laboratory in Pasadena, NASA had just instituted the Vega program which was intended to develop spacecraft technology for lunar and planetary probes. Whereas the Goddard Space Flight Center was more or less the theoretical center of the space sciences program, JPL was the engineering center, and had gathered one of the finest engineering teams in the world. The importance of teamwork in a space mission cannot be overemphasized.

JPL was also planning the Mariner A program which had Venus as its goal, and Mariner B, aimed for Mars. After a year of intensive work, the Vega and Mariner programs were revised for a very interesting reason. They had been predicated on the use of the Centaur rocket as the launch vehicle, but the Centaur used liquid hydrogen for fuel and was tricky to handle. When the Air Force engineers developed the Agena rocket, which used liquid oxygen and was more reliable, it was decided to switch to the Agena. Also, the theoreticians had just developed the "Parking Orbit" concept, which was adopted.

I mentioned the Parking Orbit earlier, and it's a fascinating technique now used in all launches. Instead of attempting to put the spacecraft into orbit or trajectory with one continuous operation, you break it down into two steps. First the craft is boosted into a circular orbit around the earth. This is the Parking Orbit. You can wait for a few seconds or a few minutes or even a few hours while you look things over and catch your breath, so to speak. The craft is quietly circling the earth. You then pick your moment to deliver the final thrust which will insert it into its planned course.

As a result of these theoretical and technical advances, JPL changed the Vega program to a mission they called Ranger Block I and Block II. This was their working title. We know them as the first five Ranger Moon probes. Mariner A became Mariners I and II, the Venus probes, and Mariner B became Mariners III and IV, the Mars probes.

At the Goddard Space Flight Center, which was just being built, they were discussing the communications satellites — Telstar, Syncom, and Relay — the Orbiting Geophysical Observatory, OGO (pronounced "Oh-go"), the Orbiting Astronomical Observatory, OAO (pronounced "O.A.O."), the advanced Tiros and Nimbus weather satellites, and, of course, the Orbiting Solar Observatory, OSO, which was already underway.

Originally NASA planned to limit the OSO family to two satellites because the program had a very low budget. Hogarth thinks this was just as well. "It wasn't in the seventy-million-dollar class like OAO, which bothers John. He goes South and sees unpainted shacks, and he worries. I do, too. But this was a cheap operation, around three and a half million dollars. My God, we practically gave away Green Stamps!"

The design and specifications of S-16 and S-17 (remember, these were the working titles of the first two members of the OSO family) were drafted under Lindsay's supervision, and he planned to fly eight Goddard experiments aboard S-16. There was room for five more. Proposals were solicited, and additional experiments by the University of Minnesota, University of Rochester, University of California, and the Ames Research Center were accepted by the Steering Committee. By midsummer of 1959 Lindsay's pet project was completely organized. But before describing the construction of the satellite and the experiment packages, let me take time out to trace the development of the vehicle that was to carry them into space. After all, there's no which-came-first-the-chicken-or-the-egg enigma here; obviously the rocket had to come first.

5
Rocket Vehicles

MANY people connected with the space program tell what they claim is a true story about a little old lady who asked them, "Why does man have to go into space? Why can't he stay home on earth and watch television, the way the good Lord intended?" It's a charming legend, and one can only wonder which NASA public information officer invented it. Nevertheless, it does raise the question of how the good Lord intended man to get into space. So far the only way we can make the trip is aboard a rocket.

Rostand's Cyrano de Bergerac invented seven ways of getting up into space. Six of them are merely poetic fantasy, but one sounds remarkably prophetic: "Or — for I have some mechanic skill — To make a grasshopper with springs of steel, and launch myself by quick succeeding fires, salt-peter-fed, to the stars' pastures blue!" This might be a seventeenth-century version of a rocket.

Rockets have been around for a long time, almost as long as gunpowder. The principle of the rocket is that of action and reaction. If you explode something and constrain the outrushing gases so that they're released in only one direction, they'll have the effect of shoving whatever's exploding in the opposite direction. Kids play with this reaction effect when they explode firecrackers in empty beer cans, kicking them twenty feet into the air.

Artillerymen had been monkeying around with rockets for centuries without much success, mostly because the technology of explosives was too primitive to permit accurate control. The science never got beyond the novelty stage until the 1920's when some sort of nut named Dr. Robert Goddard (in whose honor the Goddard Space Flight Center was named) started experimenting with rockets and fuels. No one took his pioneering seriously; in fact, he was great for laughs when movie footage of his failures was shown along with wing-walking and flagpole-sitting in the newsreels that graced the twenties. Goddard published many technical papers on the theory of rocketry, but their importance was not recognized in America until much later.

In Germany, it was Hermann Oberth's book *Rockets in Planetary Space* that acted as the catalyst in the development of practical rocketry, and stimulated the formation of the German Society for Space Flight. An enthusiastic group of members, among them a youngster named Wernher von Braun, gathered around Oberth. In August, 1930, they succeeded in testing their first conical rocket motor which generated a thrust of 15.5 pounds for a period of ninety seconds. Their experiments eventually culminated in the V-2 rocket center in Peenemünde, and the dreaded buzzbomb which was Hitler's last-ditch weapon in World War II. When, after the war, the Peenemünde engineers were shown the scores of Goddard papers and patents which had been kept secret until then, they were amazed at their similarity to many of the features of the V-2.

This is as good a time as any to exorcise the myth that the USSR is ahead of the United States in the space race because their German scientists are better than ours. Walter Wiesman, one of the original Peenemünde group, recalls those last days of the war vividly. "When the Russians were closing in on the east, and the Allies on the west, the high command decided to move the V-2 station into central Germany for protection. The entire staff was given the choice of remaining in Peenemünde in the east, or going west. Not one key man elected to remain in Peenemünde. The relatively few people the Russians got were unimportant. They simply picked up the leftovers."

Wiesman was also anxious to clear up another sore point, the charge that the Peenemünde scientists had been Nazis. He said, "Long before the war Hitler passed a law that made all organizations in Germany automatic members of the Nazi party. It didn't matter what it was; automobile club, rocket club, fraternal society. I was a boy scout when the law was passed, and I woke up and found out I belonged to the Nazi party. The same thing happened to almost everybody."

The American Army captured the V-2 equipment in central Germany, and managed to get von Braun and his team out of the country just in the nick of time. All of them signed work contracts with the Army. Von Braun and six men flew to the Aberdeen Proving Grounds and helped process German guided missile documents. They evaluated tons of papers, charts, and drawings. When the captured hardware of about a hundred V-2's arrived at White Sands, the seven were transferred to Fort Bliss, Texas, where the rest of von Braun's team, over a hundred men, joined them in late 1945 and early 1946.

Then there was an impasse. The Army was anxious to learn all it could about rocketry and guided missiles from von Braun's group, but the V-2 was a military weapon, and America had just fought a war in the hope and belief that there would be no more wars. Congress could not be persuaded to allocate an adequate budget for rocket research and development. Research and development, usually abbreviated to R&D, are the two most crucial words in the twentieth century. Without a yeasty R&D program no enterprise of any sort stands a chance of survival, let alone progress.

Wiesman said, "It was impossible for America to admit that weapons development should continue. It took the Korean War to change its point of view. But in the meantime we were just sitting there. The waiting! The waiting! We had all this knowledge and we weren't permitted to use it."

During those years of waiting, the von Braun team fired their V-2's at White Sands and Cape Canaveral, and were allowed to try a few experiments. They launched rhesus monkeys in nose cones, proved out the step-rocket theory by mounting a WAC Corporal rocket on the nose of a V-2 and attaining a record altitude of two hundred fifty miles, and worked with an unknown scientist named Dr. James Van Allen who climbed around the nose cones of the V-2's, sticking in Geiger counters wherever he could find room, to test the theory of a radiation belt around the earth which he'd formulated.

In 1950, von Braun's team, called the Development Operations Directorate, was transferred to the abandoned army arsenal in Huntsville, Alabama. The local businessmen, who had been hoping for a major army installation, were thunderstruck when they found out they were getting a parcel of Germans fooling around with rockets. One of them said, "What a letdown! But the good Lord knew best. Now we wouldn't trade this for anything." Indeed not. In ten years Huntsville's prosperous population has grown from 12,000 to 130,000, and business is booming.

"The Germans came to look Huntsville over," he went on, "and they loved the country. They moved in. They were destitute, but they pooled their resources and bought thirty-six acres of land for seventy-two hundred dollars to build homes, and they built some beautiful places. The natives call it 'Sauerkraut Hill.' "

But by this time von Braun had used up all his V-2's. The army allocation for rocket research was very small, around three hundred thousand dollars a year. His group had no major program, and very little work to do. They watched enviously while another Army group fired missiles downrange into the woods and scrubland that lay between the arsenal and the Tennessee River. The military police kept this area cordoned off for safety's sake, and this made it a haven for moonshiners who set up their stills there. Apparently they were willing to run the risk of getting clobbered by a rocket as a trade-off for the guarantee that no Rev'nooers would be around.

By 1951 the Korean War had changed our attitude toward weapons R&D. Von Braun's budget was increased, and he was instructed to develop a long-range artillery rocket. His group produced the Army's first large ballistic missile, the Redstone. This was a liquid-fuel rocket using alcohol and water, with liquid oxygen as the oxidizer. The team painstakingly handmade the rockets, one by one, and fired them for the army. The first Redstone was launched at Cape Canaveral in August, 1953.

By now von Braun was getting restive. He wasn't interested in rockets as military weapons; he was interested in them as space vehicles. He got together with Navy officers in informal secret sessions and cooked up a plan to launch a small space satellite. The Navy was to build the payload, and von Braun would launch it with a souped-up Redstone capped with solid-propellant upper stages. This was called Project Orbiter. Von Braun was positive that the Orbiter vehicle could achieve the engineer's dream, earth-orbital velocity.

At this point the space picture became clouded by service rivalries. The International Geophysical Year was being planned, and the IGY science committee approached President Eisenhower with a project for launching an IGY satellite. There were competing proposals from von Braun, the Navy, the Air Force, and the Naval Research Laboratory, and fierce lobbying broke out. The president was forced to appoint a committee to judge between the rival proposals.

The committee selected the Navy Vanguard project, and all others were ordered to cease and desist. Von Braun was assigned the job of developing a new fifteen-hundred-mile Jupiter missile to replace the Redstone. He obeyed orders, but also continued work on the Orbiter rocket, claiming it would support the Jupiter project. To be politic he renamed it Jupiter-C. When the Jupiter work was completed, he also had two additional Jupiter-C's stored in a warehouse. He denies that it was a bootleg operation.

In October, 1957, Sputnik went up, and the entire picture at the arsenal changed overnight. It was a dramatic moment. Neil McElroy was replacing Charles Wilson as Defense Secretary, and was at Huntsville inspecting the arsenal installations. He was at dinner in the officers' club with the staff and local political leaders when the news broke. It was a bombshell.

"Congressmen came to von Braun," one eyewitness reports, "with their hands outstretched, asking, 'Doctor! What should we do? What should we do?' "

McElroy asked von Braun how long it would take to launch a satellite.

"Seventy days," von Braun answered. After all, he had his Jupiter-C's stashed in the warehouse.

"Now wait a minute," General Medaris, the army ballistics commandant, said. "Let's be safe and say ninety days."

Eighty-four days later, the von Braun group launched Explorer I, which had been built by JPL, with the Jupiter-C vehicle. The country breathed a sigh of relief, but the Peenemünde immigrants were chagrined. They had become dedicated American citizens. (Many of them are prominent Huntsville do-gooders.) They knew that they and their native-born colleagues were the best rocket engineers in the world. They felt that their team had been hopelessly handicapped by America's reluctance to sponsor rocket research. They had been particularly hurt by President Eisenhower's comment when he was told about Russia's Sputnik. "No wonder," he had said, "with those German scientists they're using."

"That irked us because it lulled America," Wiesman said. "It almost killed the space program. The Russians picked up the leftovers from Peenemünde, brainwashed them, and *worked*. We did not. There were six cold years of waiting, while the Russians went ahead. Only the Korean War forced us to face facts. By then it was too late to catch up." Today America is bitterly regretting that delay.

By the middle of 1958 the Defense Department finally gave von Braun the go-ahead on the Saturn I rocket, and allowed him ten million dollars for its development. But Saturn was a space vehicle, not a missile, and the Army really didn't know what to do with it. Therefore, when NASA was set up, they offered the project to them. President Eisenhower asked Congress to allow the transfer, and on July 1, 1960, von Braun's team went over to NASA. Their installations at the arsenal were leased from the DOD by NASA, and renamed the George C. Marshall Space Flight Center, by special request of President Eisenhower.

One of the arsenal officers said, "We lost three thousand top men, and a hundred and fifty million dollars in concrete to Marshall. It was a lot of surgery."

But one of von Braun's aides says, "For the first time in his life the Old Man (von Braun was not yet fifty) wasn't working for generals. He was his own boss, and he had a budget." He did indeed. It rose in giant leaps from four hundred thousand dollars a year to nearly two billion a year as America tried desperately to overtake the Russians after having given them a six-year headstart.

It must be apparent by now that although missile R&D and space R&D are conducted separately, both use rockets as the vehicles to carry their payloads. For the most part, missiles use solid-fuel rockets because they must be storable, and liquid fuels are very difficult to keep. Liquid oxygen must be maintained at $-297°$ F., and liquid hydrogen at

—423° F.; otherwise they boil off and turn into unusable gas.

Missiles are designed in a variety of sizes, depending on the required range and the weight of the warhead. Some are so small that they can be fired from the shoulder. Redeye is a two-stage antiaircraft missile which homes in on the infrared heat of an enemy plane engine. It's four feet long, three inches in diameter, and can be transported and operated by a single man. At the arsenal they say that in the Marshall program the missiles carry the men, and in the Army program the men carry the missiles.

The Air Force has developed larger systems carrying heavier payloads over longer distances, and it is mostly these which NASA buys for launch vehicles. There are about ten in the NASA stable, some of which were developed under direct NASA supervision. Here are the vehicles, their payload capabilities computed for an orbit one hundred miles above earth, and the prime contractors who build them.

Vehicle	*Payload*	*Contractors*
Scout	300 lbs.	Chance-Vought
Thor-Delta	1,000 lbs.	Douglas Aircraft
Thor-Agena	2,000 lbs.	Douglas Aircraft
Atlas-Mercury	3,000 lbs.	General Dynamics
Atlas-Agena	5,000 lbs.	General Dynamics
Titan II	7,000 lbs.	Martin
Atlas-Centaur	12,000 lbs.	General Dynamics
Saturn I	22,500 lbs.	Chrysler, Douglas Aircraft
Titan IIIC	25,000 lbs.	Martin
Saturn IB	36,000 lbs.	Chrysler, Douglas, I.B.M.
Saturn V	250,000 lbs.	Boeing, Douglas, North American Aviation, I.B.M.

There's a reciprocal relationship between rocket thrust, payload weight, and distance desired, which governs the selection of a particular rocket for a particular mission. For example, the Energetic Particles Explorer, EPE, was a hundred-pound satellite. You might think that the Scout, with its three-hundred-pound payload capacity, would be more than adequate to put the satellite into orbit, and so it would for an orbit one hundred miles above the earth, but the EPE was intended to measure radiation belts extending out 9,000 miles from the earth. Consequently, the Thor-Delta, with a thousand-pound payload capacity, was used as the vehicle. The extra capacity provided the extra mileage.

When von Braun's team was taken over by NASA it was ordered to develop large space vehicles. Von Braun at last was in a position to accelerate the Saturn program which he had begun with the Army two years before. This program progressed through a series of three successively larger vehicles to the mightiest rocket of them all, the Saturn V. It's interesting to compare this juggernaut with the tiny Army Redeye antiaircraft missile.

Redeye is three inches in diameter, you remember; Saturn V is thirty-three feet in diameter. Redeye is four feet long; Saturn V stands thirty-six stories high with its payload. The United Nations building in New York is only three stories higher. Redeye is a two-stage missile; Saturn V is a three-stage vehicle. The lowest, or booster stage, has five engines, each about the size and shape of a palatial South Sea Island hut, which will burn liquid oxygen and kerosene for 150 seconds and bring the craft up to 6,000 MPH before separation.

The second stage has five engines burning liquid oxygen and liquid hydrogen. They will burn for over 400 seconds, bringing the craft up to 14,000 MPH before separation. The third stage has a single engine which is to be ignited twice. The first burn will bring the craft up to 17,500 MPH, which is just enough to put it into a Parking Orbit around the earth. The second burn will accelerate the craft to 25,000 MPH and send it on its journey into space. This is the vehicle designed for the Apollo mission to the moon.

The rockets are guided by swiveling their engines to alter the direction of their thrust. Since a man's reflexes are much too slow for the millisecond responses required, the engines are controlled by computer systems in the rockets. The course that the vehicle is to fly is programmed into the computer which then responds to any deviation and corrects it by altering the thrust angle.

The deflection influences are tremendous. There is windshear, air turbulence, and the basic imbalance of the rocket itself. As the vehicle rises higher and higher it encounters the furious jet streams of the upper altitudes, blowing at 200 MPH. These can break up the rockets, which are very lightly constructed — they're hardly more than thin skins of metal containing the fuel.

The liftoff itself presents difficulties. The craft does not rise smoothly; rather it whips and vibrates very much the way a long, slender javelin does when it's thrown. The danger here is that the computer will attempt to correct for this vibration and throw itself into an hysteria of overcorrection. To guard against this, the vehicle is suspended in a tower and shake-tested to simulate the vibrations of the launch. Its computer system is then programmed to ignore these normal stresses and strains.

Bill Schindler is a Thor-Delta expert at Goddard, and he has this to say about rocketry: "If you go to a shooting gallery, the muzzle velocity of your gun is around two thousand feet per second. A launch has ten times that; twenty thousand feet per second. The magic number for orbital velocity is twenty-five thousand feet per second, or five miles per second. At that velocity a bullet could orbit the earth five feet above the ground, and a satellite at one hundred miles above the ground. This is for circular orbits. Elliptical orbits demand more velocity because their apogees are farther out. They require six miles per second."

(The point in an orbit farthest from earth is called the apogee, from *apo* — from, away — and *geo* — the earth. The point in the orbit that comes closest to earth is called the perigee, from *peri* — around, about.)

"Right now," Schindler continued, "our Deltas are limited to putting one thousand pounds into low orbits. They could send a hundred and fifty pounds to the moon, and a hundred and thirty pounds in just plain escape . . . escape in the sense of total escape from the earth's gravity."

On vehicle guidance Schindler said, "You don't aim in one direction, you steer it as it goes. From liftoff to burnout you have five minutes for steering. You have extreme velocity only in the last minute or so. In practice you shoot vertically to get out of the atmosphere. Then you bend over in the direction you want to go. Then you jockey for altitude, angle, and the velocity you want at burnout. You have to know how fast you're going to a tenth of a per cent. You aim, you sense when you have enough velocity, and you cut off."

As an illustration of how critical velocity is, take the case of the Interplanetary Monitoring Probe. IMP was an interplanetary explorer intended, among other things, to assist the Apollo Moon Mission by assessing radiation hazards and acquiring data on solar flares. Its planned orbit had an apogee of 160,000 miles. IMP failed because its final stage was one second short in burning; it burned for twenty-nine seconds instead of thirty seconds. The loss of that one second of acceleration dropped the apogee from the planned 160,000 miles to 50,000 miles, and IMP never got far enough out into space to do its job.

"When you aim," Schindler said, "it's like running alongside a bullet and steering it as it goes. You must be accurate to within a quarter of a degree. In order to visualize this accuracy look at the sweep hand of your watch. Each minute on the dial is equal to six degrees. Say the sweep hand makes six flicks per minute. That means each flick of the second hand is equal to one degree. You must divide a single flick by four to achieve a quarter of a degree."

This accuracy demands finely tuned mechanisms. Vehicles are guided by gyroscopic control plus a program of computer commands, or ground station computer control through radar tracking, or both. "These things are basically unstable," Schindler said, referring to rockets. "Arrows are stable. You shoot them and they stay in the path. But if you shot one of these rockets like an arrow it would tumble over and over. It has to do with the center of gravity. Rockets work like weather vanes; they have a tendency to head into the wind."

Another of the constraints of boost orbits is that the burned-out stages must land in the ocean. There have been one or two cases of stages falling on land. Fidel Castro screamed that it was an act of outright aggression when a launch from the Cape misfired and landed on a Cuban farm. Africa received another accidental gift from the Cape; rocket casings strewn across miles of barren country. They raised hell, too.

"But people will just have to get used to the idea that they're going to get hit by falling stages," Schindler said, "just as they're getting hit by falling planes. Fortunately a good proportion of the stages burn out in the air, but within the next few years spent rockets and satellites are going to start dropping back to earth. Space people are worried about this."

These fragments are already beginning to fall. They're called "decayed objects" because their orbits have decayed as a result of the earth's gravitational attraction which slowly pulls them down. When they reenter the atmosphere, the smaller objects burn up like meteorites. They don't come diving in; they skip in over the upper atmosphere, like a flat stone over water, which gives them time to burn, and gives rise to flying saucer reports featuring Little Green Men. All reports are processed by the Smithsonian Astrophysical Observatory.

It's the larger objects that are the headache; they come down without skipping. One of them smashed into the main street of a town in Manitoba. When experts were called in to find out if it was a meteor, they discovered that it was a chunk of Sputnik IV. The Canadians sent it back to Russia without thanks.

6

Building a Satellite

Now back to OSO, the Orbiting Solar Observatory. The first member of the family was S-16, and the Ball Brothers research group at Boulder, Colorado, began work on S-16 in September, 1959. It was a "sole-source" operation.

Ordinarily, when NASA builds a spacecraft, they first define their needs and then issue a request to private industry for proposals, or bids. The Source Selection Board acts as a jury and evaluates the proposals. A contract will not necessarily go to the lowest bidder. "We're buying talent." NASA says, giving the lie to the story about the astronaut lifting off in his Mercury capsule and hollering, "My God! All this was built by the lowest bidder!"

Around 85 per cent of the construction work is done by private industry; "out-house," NASA calls it; 15 per cent is done "in-house," that is, by the NASA engineers and technicians at the Jet Propulsion Laboratory, Goddard, Huntsville, and other centers. They do this to make sure they'll stay ahead of the art (and satellite-building is an art; make no mistake) and be able to supervise out-house contractors with expertise. As one Source Selection Board member puts it, "We don't want to become a mere papermill, like the Air Force." NASA feels that the inexperience of the armed forces supervisors in the early days of the missile program enabled private contractors to take advantage of them. This is no longer true today, but NASA isn't taking any chances.

Occasionally the space projects are given to contractors without competitive bidding. Hogarth, the OSO Project Manager, said, "There are many factors involved. Competition can be a waste of time and money. The request for bids and the submission and consideration of proposals takes ages. Often a successful bidder proves to be out of his depth for the work he proposes to do, and he must be supported with advice and financing to enable him to deliver. This may involve an expensive delay.

"On the other hand, it may be considered expedient by the procurement people to let contracts on the basis of competitive bidding because rival firms bring political pressure on their congressmen. However, there was no question about doing business exclusively with Ball Brothers, and sole-sourcing the OSO satellites."

The reason for this was the fact that the research group at Boulder, usually called BBRC for Ball Brothers Research Corporation, had come up with the original plan for Lindsay's satellite. Their theoretician, O. E. Bartoe, had designed it and worked out the dynamics of the system. Then Fred Dolder, a practical engineer, joined him and evolved techniques for the physical realization of the concept. All this had been done in response to NASA's query as to whether their rocket-pointing control could be adapted to a satellite. Bartoe says, "I visualize myself as the father of OSO, and Fred Dolder as the mother. My job only took a few weeks, but the gestation took several years, and was much harder work."

The original design of the satellite was very modest. It called for a small craft with a limited life in space of only three weeks. As problems arose, one after the other, BBRC discovered that they could only be solved by increasing the size, weight, and life of the satellite. The final design of S-16 matured into a highly sophisticated form.

It was like nothing ever seen on earth before, and might easily have given rise to flying saucer legends. At first glance you would think it was an enormous open fan sitting on top of a spinning raft. Visualize a half-circle, three feet in diameter and about a foot thick. BBRC called this fan structure the "sail" because, like a ship's sail always turned to the wind, it was always to face the sun.

The sail is on a large central pivot and sits on top of a nine-sided drum. The drum is shallow; three feet in diameter and about a foot deep. BBRC called it the "wheel" because, like a wheel, it was to be constantly revolving. Three arms project out from the wheel, like outrigger arms, and each holds at its end a large metal bottle of compressed gas.

The wheel was designed to spin at thirty revolutions per minute in order to provide a stable platform for the sail. This produced a gyroscopic effect, the only way to guarantee that the satellite would remain upright in space; in fact it's the only way that anything can remain rigidly fixed in space. The reason the earth doesn't topple over and over is the fact that it revolves. The revolution of the wheel, or "spin-up" as the engineers call it, was to be produced by gas jets released from the bottles at the ends of the outrigger arms.

While the wheel spun, the sail was to sit on top of it and

keep its face pointed at the sun. It would not revolve with the wheel because servomotors, regulated by the pointing control, would drive the sail in the opposite direction to the wheel's spin. However, when the craft passed into the dark side of the earth, the servomotors would switch off automatically, to conserve power and reduce wear on the bearings. When OSO came back into the light, the sail would be locked on the sun once more.

This seems like a rather complicated way of going about pointing instruments at the sun, and it is. Unfortunately, there was no other way to design the satellite. Two incompatibles had to be reconciled. The observatory in the sail had to point at the sun constantly and motionlessly. In order to do this it had to be mounted on a rock-steady platform. The only way the platform could be kept steady in space was by making it spin. Therefore the sail had to counterspin. The immovable and movable had to be combined.

The sail carried an array of solar cells on its face to generate electric power from sunlight, its pointing controls, and 75 pounds of experimental instruments for the examination of the sun itself. The wheel accommodated the communications, control, and maintenance equipment of the satellite and an additional 100 pounds of instruments for experiments which would not be affected by the wheel's spin. The entire satellite was 92 inches in diameter, 37 inches high, and weighed a little over 450 pounds. It was to be launched with a Delta rocket vehicle into a nearly circular orbit 350 miles above the earth with a period of ninety minutes. It was hoped that OSO would live for at least six months.

S-16 was scheduled to be launched in September, 1961, allowing two years for the completion of the job. No one realized that they were dreaming, and that the schedule would embarrass them when the GAO (the General Accounting Office) reviewed their work.

Robert Benchley once wrote an amusing piece about the predicament of a man who knows nothing about engineering, but who agrees to build a bridge for a town, mostly because he's a nice guy who just can't say no to anyone. The congratulations and testimonial dinners are all very pleasant, but what happens when they escort the man to the bank of the river, shake hands, and leave him? What then? What does he do next?

The Ball research group was faced with a similar dilemma. How do you go about building something you've never built before; in fact, something that no one has ever built before? They attacked it by feeling their way into the project with exploratory experiments, expedients, and makeshifts. R. H. (Gabe) Gablehouse, the Boulder program manager on OSO, says, "When OSO started, Ball had less than fifty men at Boulder, mostly engineers. We set about to build S-16 ourselves, literally, which got us into trouble later on. We built it like you build something in the back of a garage.

"We didn't really keep records of exactly why and how everything was done. This made trouble when it came time to build the next one, because when we said, 'We've got to do it this way, the other won't work. We know because we tried it,' we were asked to show our records, and the records were all in our head."

The Boulder engineers began with a prototype, to be followed by a flight model of the satellite. The prototype runs interference for the flight model, so to speak. It's approached by successive approximations. When the engineers feel that they've got the design set, the flight model is patterned on the final version of the prototype. The backup or spare is a replica of the flight model.

The prototype is also used for extremely severe tests. It undergoes preliminary environmental tests at one and a half times the stress that the flight model is expected to experience in space, and for twice as long as it's expected to endure it. This is one reason why the construction of satellites takes so long; the tests go on endlessly. On the other hand, the flight model is tested well below the limits of its strength so as not to fatigue and weaken it.

In the beginning, the construction of S-16 was almost happy-go-lucky. "It was a simple affair," Hogarth says, "because no one had any idea of how to go about the job. S-16 just sort of grew."

But it grew into frightful complications. "It was originally planned to last three weeks because we had only one experiment aboard," Fred Dolder recalls. "But then the concept changed. We discovered that we needed more mass for the spin-up, so instead of the satellite weighing a hundred pounds, it became five hundred pounds. Instead of one experiment we had a dozen. The problems were quadrupled, but we were too dumb to know it."

The first problem was structure. They decided to use aircraft-type aluminum alloy for plates and castings. They discovered that the plates used for decks developed hairline cracks under stress. They were forced to change the components of the aluminum alloy and switch to magnesium for some structural parts. They discovered that it was almost impossible to get good castings of light alloys which were needed for the gimbal arrangement in which the pointing control and sail experiments were to be swung in azimuth and altitude.

(You'll be hearing these expressions used quite often by spacemen, and they're easy to understand. When you're watching a tennis game, and swiveling your head left and right to watch the ball passing back and forth across the net, you're moving your head in azimuth. If the ball is lobbed high into the air and you crane your head back to watch it, you're moving your head in altitude. Now back to alloys.)

"Pouring an aluminum casting with the structural integrity we needed at high stress points is very difficult," Gablehouse explained. "You X-ray and hope you can see the structural defects, but you're never quite sure that you've got a good casting. It machines beautifully, but you don't know what you've got under the surface.

"We tried a local Denver man first. He was a small founder, the arty type with everything in his head, but the trouble with this type is that they can't give you quality control. So then we tried a St. Louis foundry which had a larger and more controlled operation. They were able to produce the castings, but then . . ." Gabe shook his head wearily, "then the damn foundry burned to the ground and destroyed all our patterns and castings."

Another annoying problem was the bottles in which the nitrogen gas for the spin-up maneuver was to be stored. "At first we used fiberglass spherical bottles with a rubber liner. The trouble with them was that their shelf life was limited; after six months on the shelf they began to leak. I think this was a problem of process control, too. The manufacturer was apt to make mistakes."

Unable to get quality control in the manufacture of fiberglass bottles, and unable to use steel bottles because they were too heavy, the Boulder engineers went out on a limb and gambled on spherical titanium bottles. "They had to have very thin walls and had to be made exactly right, or they blew up." Gablehouse said. "The metallurgy of titanium is still primitive today; we really don't know much about how to handle the metal.

"We needed to add a protective coating because titanium is extremely sensitive to scratch, so we bought basketballs and used them to cover the bottles." Gabe grinned. "Word got out that we were going to launch basketballs into space, and we got a lot of mail on that. Of course we didn't fly the basketballs. They were just protection."

Since the satellite had moving mechanical parts, it had to be lubricated. "The lubrication problems were awesome," Bob Mattingly of the spacecraft integration division at Goddard says. "Hard vacuum is the basic phenomenon that gives the most trouble. At five hundred miles out, things begin to happen. Certain metals will cold-weld, and gear teeth will pull chunks out of each other. Certain elements in metals will outgas, that is, boil off. Ultraviolet light and the Van Allen radiation will decay and rot metals and plastics.

"Gold on gold is a self-lubricant . . . it's not understood how this operates . . . but you need a very hard gold that won't wash off. Dry powders such as molybdenum disulphide can be used; the molecules orient in such a way as to act as a lubricant. Silicones are advocated, but silicon must be replenished, has limited 'wetting' capabilities, and has a tendency to boil off at lower vacuums.

"It's a question of balancing your requirements. We ended up using a hydrocarbon lubricant on S-16. There was a danger of its filming optical surfaces, but that seemed small compared to the problems of the other candidates. We used Bardahl."

Lindsay explained that it wasn't the commercial Bardahl for cars that was used. "It was the special ingredient in it that they sent us. It was suggested that we fly an 'oily rag' and we did this. We used an oil reservoir."

Gablehouse elaborated on this. "Actually we used a combination of Bardahl and another lubricant which the manufacturer said we shouldn't use." Gabe snorted. "We used it anyway, and it worked, which just shows that he didn't know what he was talking about." In all fairness it must be pointed out that in those pioneering days nobody really knew what they were talking about. It was all trial and error.

The complexities continued to compound themselves. Could they stabilize the wheel with the gyroscopic spin-up enough to make it a rigid platform for the instruments? Could its stability withstand the two strongest forces that would act on the craft — magnetic torque and the gravity gradient torque? The satellite wants to point like a compass needle in the earth's magnetic field, and constantly yearns for a north-south alignment. This is magnetic torque. The earth's gravitational field pulls harder at the bottom of the satellite than the top (because it's closer) and the satellite wants to tumble. This is the gravity gradient torque.

These effects are minute but extremely important because it is force multiplied by time that's working against you. The compass pull on a satellite would be almost unnoticeable in the course of a few days, but after a hundred days it would pile up into a gross change in attitude or aim. Just to point this up, if the mathematicians who plotted the trajectory of the Mariner Mars probe had not allowed for the minute effect of light pressure from the sun, the five-hundred-pound spacecraft would have been pushed twelve thousand miles off course by the end of its flight.

The gravity gradient torque problem had to be left to the spin-up. Either the gyroscopic stability of the wheel would keep the observatory aimed at the sun, or it wouldn't; only the actual flight would tell. Everybody crossed their fingers. The magnetic torque could be nullified by deperming or demagnetizing the craft.

First a contour map of the magnetic field of the satellite is plotted. One of the devices used to do this is a pendulum carrying a tiny pea-lamp on its bob. The pendulum is suspended over portions of the satellite and swung. As the magnetic field attracts the steel bob it alters its path. Photographic film is exposed in a camera for the duration of the oscillations, and the pea-lamp traces a pattern of light curves on the film which reveals the focus and intensity of the attraction. On the basis of the contour map, the craft is placed in a giant electro-coil in various positions to wipe out its permanent magnetic fields, or deperm it.

Electric power was to be provided by a solar array of cells which operate on the same principle as the silicon solar cells in the pointing control. Sunlight produces a charge in the cells which is stored in batteries. The principle is also similar to the hookup of generator and battery in an automobile, but with one big difference. The solar array of a satellite, producing 30 watts of power, costs $48,000, or $1600 per watt; you can buy a car generator for $60, or $10 per watt.

Batteries turned out to be another frustration; in fact, battery failure is one of the main causes of the death of spacecraft. The OSO design was seven cells in aluminum blocks, and a total of six blocks. They cost $125 each, and cost from $400 to $500 to test. The Boulder engineers found that more often than not they had a 100 per cent rejection rate. In other words, they were so completely inadequate that there was no hope of improving their performance. "Batteries are still in the Stanley Steamer age, and we desperately need a breakthrough in battery technology. This is one reason why we're thinking of going over to nuclear power for spacecraft in the future."

It was decided to use a radio tone command system for controlling S-16 and its experiments. In the ordinary tone system you broadcast a radio signal at so many kilocycles. The transmitted tone makes a reed vibrate, and the vibration operates a relay in the satellite. Each command uses a different signal, and there were forty commands required for S-16. No one had any way of knowing that this system would open the door for a freak disaster unparalleled in spacecraft history; a satellite utterly bewildered by an unknown voice speaking to it from nowhere.

Data from the experiments was to be stored in a tape recorder. The recorder had an endless tape in a loop, some eight hundred feet long. It was to record data for ninety minutes, the duration of one orbit, at low speed in order to save space on the tape. It would broadcast at high speed, "dumping" its ninety minutes of information in four minutes as it passed over a tracking station, and then go back to slow recording again.

Two tape recorders were planned. Lindsay said, "But how do you get a tape recorder running on a single watt of power for six months, and only measuring eight inches by four inches? The subcontractor made a fixed-price bid and lost twice as much as he bid." The recorders cost NASA $33,000 each.

Electronic equipment in spacecraft is expensive because of the amount of man-hours that go into the construction. It takes four hundred hours to put together a printed circuit board, and if only one component is damaged or fails in any way, the entire board must be scrapped. Nothing can be salvaged because the stress and strain of removing and reusing the components will weaken them far more than their probable life in space.

The danger of stress and strain in the manufacture is so critical that women are not permitted to work on delicate components during their menstrual periods; engineers dare not run the risk of subjecting the components to the extra acidity of women's skin at those times of the month. Women, by the way, are remarkably well suited to delicate electronic techniques, but display a very human weakness. After six or eight months on the job many of them become bored by the niggling work, get careless, and have to be fired.

One of the most critical areas in circuitry is solder connecting. Whenever you have a failure of any sort in a satellite, the first thing you do is check the connections. The solderers are trained and repeatedly tested and requalified. Often when a man comes back from vacation he must be sent to class again to polish his old skill. Many contractors are trying to duck this problem with "hard wiring," which is one-piece wiring without connections. Another expedient is "potting," which is a process of sealing the wiring inside plastic, like vegetables in aspic.

The nightmare of satellite construction, as the Ball

Brothers Research Corporation discovered, is contamination, and to avoid contamination almost all work is done in sterile conditions. Surgical caps, gowns, and slippers are worn, and test benches and chambers are ventilated by lamina flow. This is produced by baffles at one end of a room which keep the incoming ventilation parallel to the floor so that no dust will be raised. At the other end of the room the air is collected, filtered, and circulated around to the baffles where it comes in as lamina flow again.

The dangers of contamination have a very interesting basis. Mattingly of Goddard explains, "In the early years of the space program we attempted to counter the hostile environment of space by carrying terrestrial environment out into space, using sealed experiments. Then we discovered that this raised so many problems that it had to be abandoned. Now the attempt is to adapt the experiments to the actual environment of space."

When you send spacecraft and experiments out into space they must be as free from contamination as space is itself. There can be no dust whatever. Dust particles can attract gas molecules. Gas molecules can originate from the outgassing of fingerprints, and remain within the satellite as a gas atmosphere. X-ray and gamma-ray experiments use comparatively high amounts of voltage and require a total absence of atmosphere so that there will be no path for a high-voltage arc.

Perhaps the most dramatic dust incident took place while the Mariner IV probe was en route to Mars. The craft's attitude or position in space was controlled by its "Canopus sensor." This was a pointing device operating on the same principle as a sun sensor, but using the star Canopus as its reference point. The sensor searched through the stars, rejecting all those that were too faint or too bright, until finally it found Canopus and locked on it.

Unfortunately there was dust on the probe, or dust had been knocked off its solar array by the impact of micrometeorites — no one knows the origin for sure — and the dust began to orbit the spacecraft. Sunlight made the motes shine like stars, and the Canopus sensor began to chase them madly. The control center at JPL finally had to send a command to the sensor to stop thinking and stay with Canopus.

Tiny droplets of solder can cause short circuits. Dirt in the pneumatic systems is certain death; minute specks clog the valves and never work free. Dirt and dust are ionized by sunlight and give off secondary radiation which confuses the data being sensed by the instruments. Most important of all, contamination control imposes good workmanship on the technicians, and malfunction is almost always the result of poor workmanship. Bob Baumann of Goddard says, "It all depends on the human factor, on the men who actually make the components. If they've done a faithful job, it's one thing; but if they're tired or careless or indifferent . . ."

And finally, if you have something untidy, the untidiness acts as a camouflage and prevents inspectors from uncovering genuine defects.

7

Experiments in Space

WHILE the Ball Brothers Research Corporation was struggling with the complexities of building the S-16 (OSO) prototype and flight model through late 1959 and 1960, John Lindsay was organizing his solar physics department at Goddard, building his own experiments for the craft, and supervising the construction of the other Goddard experiments. He was pushing himself hard, but the strain was concealed by his impassive exterior, his slow, easy style, and his capacity for enjoyment during the odd hours when he wasn't working.

He was also arguing his fellow maverick, Director Harry Goett, into approving an Advanced Orbiting Solar Observatory. AOSO was a tremendous concept, about on a par with OAO, the Orbiting Astronomical Observatory, in terms of sub-systems and components. To give you some idea of the instrumentation of these observatories, OAO was going to require seven computers on the ground to communicate with it, programmed with 350,000 instructions. This is three times larger than the Gemini ground computer program. Looking back now, little S-16 with its simple experiments controlled by forty commands seems very modest indeed, but at the time it was the height of sophistication.

Asked about the purpose of the original experiments planned for S-16, Lindsay loafed out for another cup of coffee, returned, sat, shoved his feet up on his desk, and drawled, "Well, when we started OSO, we put ourselves on first. Then we invited in the people who were interested in solar research, or had already been doing it with rockets, and we came up with a payload."

He relit his pipe. "But you have to understand that the majority of scientists aren't the way people think they are. You know; developing a theory about phenomena, inventing an experiment to test it, and then drawing conclusions from the results. Methodical. We were exploring rather than researching. We were making interesting measurements."

The experiments carried in the sail of S-16 were called the "Pointed" experiments, and were monopolized by Lindsay and his associates at Goddard. The wheel was divided into nine pie-shaped compartments. Three of these were needed for satellite maintenance or, as it's called, "housekeeping." Of the six remaining segments, one was taken over for another Goddard package, leaving five available for outside participation. Here are the experiments and the institutions which devised them.

POINTED

Solar soft X-ray spectrometer: 10 to 400 Å — GSFC (The Goddard Space Flight Center)

Gamma-ray detector: 100 Kev to 1.5 Mev — GSFC

Solar X-ray detector: 20 to 100 Kev — GSFC

Solar X-ray ion chamber: 1 to 8 Å — GSFC

Dust particle detector — GSFC

WHEEL

Solar radiation flux detector: 3800 to 4800 Å — GSFC

Solar ultraviolet ion chamber: 1000 to 1250 Å — GSFC

Solar gamma ray detector: 0.2 to 1.5 Mev — GSFC

Solar gamma ray detector: 50 Kev to 3 Mev — University of Minnesota

Neutron monitor — University of California

Proton-electron detector: electron energies greater than 60 Kev, and proton energies greater than 2 Mev — University of California, Lawrence Radiation Laboratory, Livermore, California

Emissive stability detector: measures thermal radiation characteristics of surfaces to determine emissivity stability of spacecraft temperature-control coatings — Ames Research Center

High-energy solar gamma-ray detector: 100 to 500 Mev — University of Rochester

Now let's examine the experiments, one by one, to see why the scientists wanted to make these particular measurements, how they intended to make them, and what they hoped to learn from them.

Solar soft X-ray spectrometer: 10 to 400 Å

Å is the symbol for the Ångström Unit, sometimes written A.U., and named for the Swedish physicist who first devised it. The A.U. is a calibration of the wavelengths in the electromagnetic spectrum, measured in meters and fractions of meters. Visually, we see between 4000 A.U. and 7000 A.U.; the upper, or shorter, 4000 wavelength limit is the blue end of our visual spectrum, the lower 7000 wavelength limit is the red end. Interestingly enough, some people are capable of seeing beyond these limits; up beyond 4000 A.U. into the ultraviolet, or down beyond 7000 A.U. into the infrared. They're much like those rare individuals who can hear the bat squeaks which sound at frequencies too high for average ears.

They tell a story about a lady who went into a delicatessen and asked for liverwurst. The clerk put a three-foot liverwurst into the slicing machine and asked her how much she wanted. "Cut," she answered. The clerk sliced six inches off the end and asked, "Enough, lady?" She said, "Cut." He sliced another six inches and asked, "Enough?" "Cut, cut," she answered. When he had sliced all the way to the middle of the liverwurst, he asked, "Enough now?" "Now," she answered, "cut me ten cents' worth."

We see ten cents' worth in the middle of the total electromagnetic spectrum. The shorter wavelengths go up into the ultraviolet, X rays (which are in the 500 to 5 A.U. range), and gamma rays. The longer wavelengths go down into the infrared (we can feel the infrared as heat down to 10,000 A.U.), microradio or radar waves, and long radio waves measuring hundreds of meters from crest to crest. I sometimes try to imagine how the world would appear if the entire electromagnetic spectrum were visible to our eyes. Scientists make it visible to their instruments.

The solar soft X-ray spectrometer was intended to measure X rays with wavelengths between 100 and 5 A.U. X rays are particles, and one of the ways of measuring particle energy is by their penetration of material. The hard, or penetrating X rays are above the soft X rays in the spectrum, between 5 and .003 A.U. As you go up into the shorter and shorter wavelengths, the energy increases. By comparison, the long radio waves down at the bottom of the spectrum are slothful.

Previous measurements from ground-based observatories and sounding rockets had indicated that short wavelengths, from 2500 A.U. on up, never reached the earth; they were absorbed by our atmosphere, which seems to block almost all our observations of phenomena in space. One physicist, complaining about the handicap of the earth's atmosphere, said, "We spend our lives looking at the universe through a dirty basement window."

Other measurements had indicated that the output of the sun was not constant in the shorter wavelengths; the sun is a faintly variable star. The fact that the shorter wavelengths were being absorbed meant that they were affecting the ionosphere in some way, but in what way? The ionosphere is the reflecting layer on which radio broadcasting depends, and this is of deep interest to the communications people. The absorption was also probably heating the upper atmosphere, but how much? This was a matter of concern to the weather people.

The spectrometer is an instrument measuring the electromagnetic spectrum the way an astronomical spectrograph measures the spectrum of visible light. The spectrograph uses film to record the light spectrum split up by prisms or diffraction gratings. The spectrometer uses an electronic detector.

Gamma-ray detector: 100 Kev to 1.5 Mev

Gamma rays are not measured in wavelengths but in terms of their energy, which is calibrated in electron volts, or "ev." An electron volt is the energy of acceleration a particle receives from one volt on a plate. Roughly, you have a plate and shoot current into it. The current will energize particles and make them shoot off the plate. The value of the electron volt is 1.5×10^6 centimeters per second, or 35,000 miles per hour. The letters K, M, and B, are merely shorthand for a thousand, a million, and a billion; 100 Kev stands for 100,000 electron volts, 1.5 Mev is 1½ million electron volts. Incidentally, when the NASA people talk salary they use this shorthand. They'll say, "You know how much so-and-so is getting paid? Fifteen K."

Gamma rays are generated by nuclear reactions somewhere in space, the result of the collision of a cosmic ray with a hydrogen atom. A cosmic ray is a proton, which is a hydrogen atom nucleus stripped of its single electron. No one knows how they're produced. They're positively charged, have an electric field, and high energy in the billions of electron volts. A cosmic ray hits a hydrogen atom and the impact produces gamma rays. Actually, gamma rays are not particles, they're photons or corpuscles of light. They have very high energy, in the neighborhood of 100 Mev.

Now here's the puzzle: although gamma rays approach the earth from all directions, they have never been positively detected as coming from the sun. This is odd because we know that the rays are produced by nuclear reactions, and the sun is an active nuclear furnace. The second sail experiment was an attempt to make this positive detection.

Solar X-ray detector: 20 to 100 Kev

Experiments flown in balloons had reported X-ray bursts from the sun. They were short-lived events, lasting only a few minutes. They seemed to coincide with radio bursts from the sun, but the process by which they're generated is not known. This was an attempt to explore the phenomena. It used a scintillation crystal and a photomultiplier. Both are basic tools of the space scientist.

The scintillation crystal works like a fluoroscope screen. A photon of light strikes it, and the energy of the impact kicks an atom in the crystal into an excited state. That is, its electrons are raised from their normal energy level, called their "ground state," to a higher level. Think of the process as a ball being whirled in a horizontal circle by a string held in your hand. If someone hits the ball with a bat, it will whirl faster and rise higher. Then it will drop back to its original level. But when electrons drop back to their normal level again, they have to get rid of that extra energy. They balance the energy budget by giving off another photon of light.

The equation for this event is: $h\nu = KI - V$, where "ν" is the symbol for the Greek letter *nu*. I mention the equation only because Albert Einstein won the Nobel prize for discovering it and not, as many people think, for his theory of relativity. Lindsay said that the Nobel committee wanted to give him the prize for the relativity theory but was afraid it might prove to be a flash in the pan, so they gave him the award for this less spectacular but safer photon-photon reaction.

Immediately behind the scintillation crystal is a cathode tube. The photon emitted from the crystal by the return of the excited electrons to their normal ground state strikes the face of the cathode and generates electrons. These in turn are driven down into the multiplier, which is a series of thin baffles.

As each electron strikes a baffle, it knocks more electrons

off. The electrons continue downward, striking lower baffles and generating more electrons until they are multiplied into a cascade at the bottom of the tube. The cascade is detected as a pulse of charge. Each pulse from the photomultiplier indicates a single photon event in the scintillation crystal up above.

Solar X-ray ion chamber: 1 to 8 Å

This is another attempt to measure X-ray radiation from the sun, this time using an ion chamber. The ion chamber is another important tool of the physicist. In some ways it's reminiscent of those paperweight globes which produce miniature snowstorm scenes when they're shaken.

The ion chamber is a globe containing gas. There is a voltage across the chamber which acts as a magnet, but the magnetic field does not attract the gas molecules because they have no charge. They are in their normal state, with the negative electrons exactly balancing the positive nucleus, and you only produce a charge when this balance is upset. This is what happens when an energy particle passes through the chamber; it knocks electrons off the atoms or molecules, which ionizes them and produces a charge, and a sort of electronic snowstorm results.

Since the electron has a negative charge, a molecule losing electrons will end up with a positive charge as a remainder of the subtraction. The electrons may add themselves to other molecules which will be given a negative charge by the surplus. The voltage collects these positively and negatively ionized molecules by magnetic attraction, and measures how fast they accumulate, which is the ion-producing capability of the radiation. A Geiger counter records the amount of the radiation.

Dust particle detector

These are not energy particles; they are physical particles of dust, and the experiment was intended to determine the direction in space from which these dust particles arrive on earth.

There are some indications that we may have dust storms in orbits around the earth and sun, and there is a small but strong school which claims that this dust is debris from the moon, driven up into space by the meteor impacts which formed the lunar craters eons ago. This debris, they say, has been slowly falling to the surface of the earth through the millenia.

They argue that it isn't necessary to send an astronaut to the moon to collect samples of its surface when we might have samples right here on earth, and they organized "Project Moon Harvest" a few years back. The theory was, take a section of the country where you don't ordinarily find rocks, and comb it, particularly for tektites, which are a very odd and special form of meteorite thought to come from the moon.

Project Moon Harvest picked Iowa and enlisted the help of farmers, wives, schoolchildren, everybody. Most of the rock samples sent in to the investigators were fulgurites, which are small masses of fused earth formed when lightning strikes the ground. There were also a few "haystack fulgurites," formed when haystacks burn. Unfortunately, nothing that could be identified as lunar material turned up.

Nevertheless, debris is constantly falling to earth from space, and any bright boy who has the time and energy can collect samples the morning after a snowstorm. Simply shovel up the surface of an acre of snow, melt it, throw away the water, and examine the particles that remain in the bottom of the pot. Some of them are very likely to be dust from space that fell during the night onto the surface of the fresh snow. You do your shoveling the morning after a snowstorm to cut to a minimum that percentage of terrestrial dust blown onto the snow by winds.

In effect, the OSO dust experiment was a snow-shoveling job, attempting to locate dust particles in space and determine the direction from which they came.

Solar radiation flux detector: 3800 to 4800 Å

The solar flux is the intensity and flow of solar radiation. This wheel experiment was a measurement of the sun's radiation in a wavelength region which is also used for the spectrographic classification of stars, in an attempt to apply our knowledge of our own sun to the interpretation of the activity of other stars.

It was a very simple and cheap experiment to construct. The Goddard people used a special photomultiplier sensitive to the 3800 to 4800 band, and masked the face of the cathode with a filter which screened out all other light.

Solar ultraviolet ion chamber: 1000 to 1250 Å

Hydrogen is the most prominent and abundant element in the universe, and many cosmogonists believe that it's the fundamental proto-matter of the universe. Hydrogen absorbs light; not visible light, but ultraviolet light in two regions of the spectrum between 1000 and 1250 A.U., called Lyman alpha and Lyman beta after their discoverer. Consequently, the hydrogen in our atmosphere absorbs most of the uv light coming from the sun, and we can't examine it from ground-based observatories. But 90 per cent of the solar flux is in the ultraviolet.

This experiment was designed to examine the sun's flux in the Lyman alpha and Lyman beta bands above the earth's opaque hydrogen curtain. It was intended to discover whether it was associated with solar flares, whether it varied, and if it affected the ionosphere.

Solar gamma ray detector: 0.2 to 1.5 Mev
Solar gamma ray detector: 50 Kev to 3 Mev

These two experiments and the gamma-ray experiment in the sail were similar; all were attempts to count the gamma rays approaching the earth, and measure their direction from space. The only difference between them was the fact that they were detecting gamma rays at different energy levels.

The reason for this overlap was the failure and withdrawal of an earlier scheduled experiment from the University of Colorado. Lindsay said, "The experimenter suddenly discovered he wasn't ready and wouldn't be ready for a long time. He was using a type of Invar for the structure of a spectroscopic experiment. (Invar is a nickel-steel alloy.) Invar creeps, at least his type did. He'd line up the optical system, leave it for a few days, come back and find it was out of alignment."

Consequently, Lindsay was forced to hustle up some last-minute packages to fill his payload quota, and duplication was unavoidable.

Neutron monitor

The two heaviest strongly interacting particles known are the proton and the neutron. Whereas protons are the nuclei of the light hydrogen atoms, neutrons are generated from the nuclei of heavier atoms when they're struck by cosmic rays. Whereas protons are stable, neutrons are radioactive and decay into a proton plus other particles within twenty minutes after their creation. If they have such a short life this means that neutrons arriving on earth from space must have been generated fairly close to us. At the time of solar flares huge quantities of protons are produced by the sun, and physicists theorize that neutrons are probably produced, too, but this isn't known for sure.

The neutron monitor from the University of California was the experiment of Dr. Wilmot (Bill) Hess, now head of the Theoretical Division at Goddard. It looked for neutrons from the sun, using diurnal variations as the test. That is, it counted neutrons from space on the sun side of the earth, and then counted them on the dark side, with the earth blocking off any that might be arriving from the sun. If there was a higher count of neutrons on the sun side, that would indicate that the sun was the source.

Proton-electron detector: electron energies greater than 60 Kev, and proton energies greater than 2 Mev

The second University of California experiment was intended to study the underside of the Van Allen radiation belt. This is a phenomenon that is a source of great interest and grief to investigators in space. Until the advent of rocketry and scientific satellites, geophysicists had believed that the earth was surrounded by a thin layer of atmospheric gas no more than one hundred miles thick. The atmosphere gradually became attenuated with higher altitude until by the time you reached a hundred miles there was nothing but empty space. Satellite exploration showed that the atmosphere extends outward for thousands of miles in a thin, electrified gas of electrons and protons that swarm along the lines of force of the earth's magnetic field and form a vast region of radiation called the magnetosphere.

The response of electrified particles to the earth's magnetic field is intricate and only partially understood today, but we do know that they are trapped in two distinct belts around the earth, called the Van Allen belts. An inner belt of high-energy protons is trapped in the magnetic field some two thousand miles above the earth at its magnetic equator. The outer Van Allen belt contains high-energy electrons, and is about ten thousand miles out from the earth. The trapping does not occur above 75° latitude north, or below 75° latitude south.

The Van Allen belts were discovered and mapped by early satellites using instruments designed by Dr. Van Allen and his colleagues, and they're still being explored. They're a source of grief to experimenters because their high-energy particles produce "noise" or static which can wreck radio transmission and data retrieval from spacecraft.

Emissive stability detectors

The Ames Research Center project was a technological experiment to help select protective coats to be used on future spacecraft for thermal control. Temperature is as much of a villain in space as hard vacuum. The sudden and extreme temperature changes that occur as a satellite orbits from the dayside into the nightside and back into the dayside of the earth can destroy most materials unless some attempt is made to exercise thermal control.

High-energy solar gamma-ray detector: 100 to 500 Mev

The University of Rochester experiment was similar to the other gamma ray experiments, except that they were looking for higher energy events up to five hundred million electron volts.

It brought the total number of experiments to be flown by S-16 to thirteen. No one was superstitious, and no one gave a thought to bad luck . . . yet.

8

Telemetry: Voices from Space

But once you've got your experiment up into space, how do you get information back from it? This comes under the heading of telemetry, from the Greek *tele*—far distant—and *metron*—to measure. Telemetry is the function of the space tracking and data acquisition network facilities, and it is accomplished through an analogue-to-digital transformation.

An analogy is a likeness or correspondence. An analogue system translates one system of measurement into a corresponding system. A clock is an analogue machine. It translates fractions of time into positions of cog wheels represented by the clock hands. Perhaps the best known analogue device, at least to the scientist, is the slide rule which translates numerical relationships into linear relationships on the rule.

In the case of telemetry, physical phenomena are measured in terms of voltage analogues. That is, temperatures, magnetic fields, particles, and so on, are sensed by instruments which translate their measurements into varying electric voltages. These voltage analogues are then transformed into digits or numbers, using the binary system which is admirably suited to radio transmission. I'll give you an example of this analogue-to-digital transformation presently; first, however, let's have a brief look at the binary number system, which is the language that spacecraft speak.

The familiar decimal system manipulates numbers in blocks of units and multiples of ten; ones, tens, hundreds, thousands, and so on. If you want to write the number of the beast (Revelation XIII:18), which is six hundred three score and six, you add six hundreds, six tens, and six units:

100	10	1
6	6	6

Or, doing the addition vertically:

6 hundreds = 600
6 tens = 60
6 units = 6
666

The binary system uses blocks of units and multiples of two; ones, twos, fours, eights, sixteens, and so on. The advantage of this system is that you never need more than one each of any block to write any number, which, therefore, can be expressed as a series of ones and zeros. Writing the number of the beast in binary:

512	256	128	64	32	16	8	4	2	1
1	0	1	0	0	1	1	0	1	0

1010011010 = 666, as vertical addition shows:

1 five hundred and twelve	=	512
1 hundred and twenty-eight	=	128
1 sixteen	=	16
1 eight	=	8
1 two	=	2
		666

A question often asked is: "Don't binary numbers read backwards?" No, they read exactly like decimals, from left to right. Once you've located the position of the extreme left-hand digit, you read down to the units. For example, to read the decimal 1,101,000 all we have to do is figure out whether the left-hand 1 is in the hundred thousand, million, or ten million block. Once we've placed it, we read the rest of the number from left to right. Similarly, to read the binary 1101000 all we have to do is figure out whether the left-hand 1 is in the thirty-two, sixty-four, or one hundred and twenty-eight block. Then we read the rest of the number right on down from left to right.

Another question frequently asked is, If the binary blocks are multiples of two, they must all be even numbers. Then how do you get an odd number? The answer should be obvious; merely add a unit. Four is 100 in binary. To get five, add a unit and you have 101.

Many people find it difficult to believe that any decimal number can be expressed in binary with a series of ones and zeros. To set their minds at rest I'll count from zero to thirty-two in binary; if we can get that far we can go all the rest of the way to infinity. On the right of each binary number I'll give the actual decimal count of the binary blocks.

The binary number seems to be longer and more complicated than the familiar decimal, but actually it's easier and

Decimal	Binary
0	0
1	1 (1)
2	10 (2 + 0)
3	11 (2 + 1)
4	100 (4 + 0 + 0)
5	101 (4 + 0 + 1)
6	110 (4 + 2 + 0)
7	111 (4 + 2 + 1)
8	1000 (8 + 0 + 0 + 0)
9	1001 (8 + 0 + 0 + 1)
10	1010 (8 + 0 + 2 + 0)
11	1011 (8 + 0 + 2 + 1)
12	1100 (8 + 4 + 0 + 0)
13	1101 (8 + 4 + 0 + 1)
14	1110 (8 + 4 + 2 + 0)
15	1111 (8 + 4 + 2 + 1)
16	10000 (16 + 0 + 0 + 0 + 0)
17	10001 (16 + 0 + 0 + 0 + 1)
18	10010 (16 + 0 + 0 + 2 + 0)
19	10011 (16 + 0 + 0 + 2 + 1)
20	10100 (16 + 0 + 4 + 0 + 0)
21	10101 (16 + 0 + 4 + 0 + 1)
22	10110 (16 + 0 + 4 + 2 + 0)
23	10111 (16 + 0 + 4 + 2 + 1)
24	11000 (16 + 8 + 0 + 0 + 0)
25	11001 (16 + 8 + 0 + 0 + 1)
26	11010 (16 + 8 + 0 + 2 + 0)
27	11011 (16 + 8 + 0 + 2 + 1)
28	11100 (16 + 8 + 4 + 0 + 0)
29	11101 (16 + 8 + 4 + 0 + 1)
30	11110 (16 + 8 + 4 + 2 + 0)
31	11111 (16 + 8 + 4 + 2 + 1)
32	100000 (32 + 0 + 0 + 0 + 0 + 0)

more economical to transmit by radio. The decimal 666 requires eighteen pulses; six each for the units, tens, and hundreds. The binary 1010011010 only requires ten pulses. But the crux of binary's role in telemetry is the fact that it can represent any number with a series of ones and zeros, and any on-off, yes-no system can produce ones and zeros.

Let's take a simple example of telemetry and see how it works. Say your experiment is designed to measure temperatures in space. Your instrument is a thermometer. It is constructed so that the top of the mercury column will make contacts at its various levels, or temperature readings, and close circuits. Each different circuit transmits a different electric voltage, so that voltage becomes the analogue for temperature. The different voltages representing temperature vary from 0 volts to 5 volts in small steps.

There is a counter controlled by a clock. (All spacecraft have a central clock which regulates all operations.) The counter counts from 0 to 127 every second. 127 may seem like a curious number, but actually it's very logical because the counting is done in seven places of binary, from zero, which is 0000000, to 127, which is 1111111. When it reaches 1111111 the next count takes it back to 0000000, and it starts all over again. Think of the odometer of your car which registers from 00,000.0 miles to 99,999.9 miles, and then returns to 00,000.0 again, but not in a second.

A circuit is arranged in the counter so that a voltage is created on a wire. This voltage mounts in discrete steps from 0 to 5 volts with each count, exactly duplicating the steps of the thermometer's voltage analogue. When the count reaches 1111111, the voltage reaches 5; when the count returns to 0000000, the voltage returns to 0. Remember, all this is taking place within one second.

The voltage from the thermometer and the voltage from the counter are fed into what's called a comparator. Here they're compared. When they are equal, the counter is stopped automatically, and whichever binary number it has reached, say 1100011 (which is 99 in decimal), is frozen. The counter has now become a register. Instantly it is interrogated by the telemetry system.

Roughly, each of the seven places or "bits" of the binary number is represented by a tiny core, which looks like a microscopic metal washer. Hair-fine wires are passed through each core, and an electric current passes through the wires. If the core is registering a zero, the current flows from south to north; if the core registers a one, it flips the current so that it flows from north to south. This is called "flip-flop," and it's the foundation of all computer activity. Incidentally, telemetry never uses spacing; that is, silence. You always send zeros if you've got nothing to say.

The cores are interrogated, one at a time, in sequence. "Are you northbound or southbound?" This is called time-commutating. From the sequence of questions we get a series of ones and zeros in answer, and these make up a binary number. The process can be performed in as little as ten microseconds (a microsecond is one millionth of a second) which is why it's easy to read the thermometer every second. However, telemetrists are never satisfied with this fantastic speed and are always trying to gain a microsecond here and there in order to save electric power. Perhaps now you can understand the joy of the engineer who gained an extra four microseconds, which I mentioned in the second chapter.

Now we have the seven bits of information which make up the binary number. The whole number is called a "word."

A series of words is called a "frame." The binary is fed into a transmitting oscillator in the spacecraft, and the transmitter broadcasts the binary back to earth, using a high note for a one, and a low note for a zero. When you listen to these broadcasts from space on a loudspeaker, they sound like a warble.

On the ground these high-low tones are recorded on tape, cleaned up (that is, static and extraneous noise are removed), rerecorded, and fed into a computer which reverses the process, translates the information back into decimal, and prints it out in long columns. To tell the truth, the data print-out from a single experiment is rather disappointing. It looks like nothing so much as a cash register receipt from a supermarket.

Tables are prepared in advance, and the decimal digit information can be interpreted immediately. Here, for example, is part of a table for reports on the pitch angle of a satellite, computed in degrees:

SATELLITE PITCH ANGLE

DIGITAL COUNT	DEGREES
114	+ 0.80
116	+ 0.65
118	+ 0.50
120	+ 0.40
122	+ 0.30
124	+ 0.15
126	0.00
128	− 0.15
130	− 0.25
132	− 0.35
134	− 0.50

etc.

Scientific spacecraft transmit information from all experiments simultaneously by multiplexing, which is the transmission of many signals within a single channel. It's the same technique which enables telephone and telegraph lines to carry many messages simultaneously, and can be best explained with an analogy to a guitar. You strum the six strings of a guitar to sound a chord. If that chord is broadcast by radio, it's possible to receive it, listen, and identify the particular note that each string sounded to form the whole chord. It's also possible to separate the notes, electronically, and record each individually.

Similarly, each experiment aboard a satellite transmits its data to a master oscillator at its own particular radio frequency, or note. The master oscillator combines them into a chord which is transmitted back to earth. There the process is reversed by computer, the individual frequencies that formed the chord are separated, and an all-channel printout of the data is produced. It looks like a giant player-piano roll filled with vertical columns of figures. From this a printout of the individual data from each experiment is made and sent to the experimenters for study and analysis.

As I mentioned before, the data is recorded on tape aboard the satellite during orbit and dumped on command as the satellite passes over a tracking station. At present NASA maintains a permanent space tracking and data acquisition network, called STADAN, stretching from Alaska to Chile, with additional stations in Australia, England, Spain, and South Africa.

Hal Hoff, associate chief of Network Engineering at Goddard, says, "Tracking is the easiest part of our business today; now the emphasis is all on telemetry. Data acquisition is today's big deal. In the old days it was the reverse. In the old days the birds used to broadcast constantly. Now they store information and dump it on command. We maintain a north-south fence from 30° north to 30° south, and every time a bird goes by, we nick it. The various tracking stations forming the network are crossroads with traffic cops."

A tracking station uses a radar network projected up overhead in a grid. There are north-south and east-west lines of radar, and as the craft passes through them, the blips which it reflects back from them give you its precise position in space. However, you must know the precise geographic position of your station to do this. Then you compare fixes from several different tracking stations, and can compute the craft's position in its orbit to within 1½ meters, and its speed to within .01 meters per second.

Deep-space tracking is a different proposition because the craft is so far away. It uses giant parabolic radio antennae, called big dishes, and transponders. The transponder is a sort of beacon. Actually, a beacon is a radio transmitter; the transponder has both a radio receiver and transmitter built into it. A signal is transmitted to the transponder at a certain frequency or wavelength. The transponder has a translator which automatically increases the frequency of the signal by a fixed ratio, and then returns it to the original source on earth.

Say the fixed ratio is 5 per cent. If the original signal is sent at 500 cycles, it will be multiplied up by 5 per cent ($500 \times .05 = 25$; $500 + 25 = 525$) and returned at 525 cycles. Back on earth you multiply the 525 cycles *down* by the same ratio, and get 500 cycles, which is the same frequency as the original signal. This tells you that the craft is stationary in space.

But the spacecraft is not stationary, and its motion away from the earth has the effect of stretching out the wavelengths of the signal which it sends back. This is the familiar Doppler Effect, named after the nineteenth-century Austrian physicist who first drew the analogy between sound coming from a moving source, and the light coming from a moving star. In our case the analogy will be with radio waves coming from a moving spacecraft.

If a locomotive blows its whistle while it passes near you, the tone of the whistle increases in pitch and then abruptly decreases. The same thing happens when a car blows its horn as it passes you. The reason for this is the fact that the approaching speed of the vehicle is added to the speed of the sound waves from its whistle or horn, crowding them together and increasing their frequency. The higher the frequency, the higher the tone. On the other hand, the speed of the receding source stretches out the sound waves and decreases their frequency. The lower the frequency, the lower the tone.

This same Doppler Effect lowers the frequency of the transponder signal returned to earth by the receding craft. Consequently, when you multiply the received signal down, you don't arrive at equality, you come out with a difference which can be measured to half a cycle, or .03 meters per second, depending on the velocity of the craft. This gives you the speed. The distance of the craft can be measured by the time lapse between the transmission of the signal from earth, and the reception of the answer.

Spacecraft have limited transmission power, and at great distances their signals are very weak. There is always the danger that they will be obscured by galactic space noise and terrestrial atmospheric noise. Therefore, frequencies from one thousand to ten thousand megacycles are used, which minimize incidental noise and give the best signal-to-noise ratios. Also, the deep-space tracking stations are located in areas as remote as possible from man-made noise.

The parabolic antenna holds the craft in the focus of a narrow radio beam; the larger the dish, the narrower the beam. The eighty-five-foot antennae at the Goldstone tracking station in California have a beam width so narrow that when they transmit a beam to the moon it only covers half the disc after having traveled 250,000 miles. These dishes are mounted on enormous steel frameworks, ten stories high, and are capable of delicate motion in elevation and azimuth. Their construction has been described as a combination of bridge-building and watchmaking.

In modern practice, the antenna tracks by beaming four narrow radio lobes around a central axis called the Boresight Line. Each lobe is separate, and the difference in the signal strengths responding to each lobe is used to determine how far the spacecraft is off the Boresight Line. These signals are also used to operate the servo system which keeps the antenna following the spacecraft. Now you know the altitude and azimuth of the craft from the bearing of the antenna, and the distance and speed by Doppler. The accuracy depends on how far off the craft is; within a mile at moon distance, and about one hundred miles at Mars distance.

Big dishes are also used to beam radar at the planets, and there's a very interesting program in progress which is mapping the surface of Venus by radar. The power used to reach out into deep space is appalling. Millstone Hill, M.I.T.'s Lincoln Laboratory radar station, can send a pulse of several megawatts. (A megawatt is one million watts; your average electric light bulb uses 75 watts.) They have to be very careful not to transmit when planes are overhead. A pulse can set fire to an airliner, and detonate explosives in military planes.

9

Orbits and Trajectories

It's taking them eighteen months to build the prototype and flight model of S-16, the first member of the OSO family, and while we're waiting it might be as well to discuss orbits and trajectories. The incredible accuracy with which the NASA experts determine the paths of their spacecraft usually amazes the average man, but anyone who's ever watched him trying to park his car will understand why.

Strictly speaking, an orbit is merely one form of a trajectory. The definition of a trajectory is the path described by a body moving under the action of given forces. An orbit happens to be the path of a spacecraft influenced by the earth's gravitational force. However, it's more convenient to reserve the term orbit for the motion of craft around the earth, and use trajectory to describe the motion of craft in deep space beyond the earth's immediate influence.

I use the word "immediate" because the fact is that everything in space influences everything else, no matter how far off it is. Distance merely attenuates the influence; it never obliterates it. The most distant star and the earth exert a faint gravitational effect on each other. Cosmologists theorize that if the universe ever runs down, the final stage will be the mutual attraction of every body in it, gathering them all together in a colossal lump which will probably explode and start everything all over again.

Meanwhile, back to orbits and trajectories. Dr. Joe Siry, head of the Theory and Analysis office at Goddard, says, "Orbit determination is comparing data with theory, which any scientific experiment does. A normal orbit is where you want the missile to go, and you must know the uncertainty to within a certain percentage.

"In effect, the launch people give us a tube where you can expect to find the satellite. They try to shoot it on a wire, but the best they can do is give us a tube with a diameter of fifty to a hundred miles. The best kind of tube is based on the accuracy of a system which works properly. The worst is the catastrophe situation where something has gone wrong.

"There is an uncertainty factor, and it rides around with the satellite as a balloon of uncertainty. As you compute the real orbit, you pinprick this balloon of uncertainty which may be hundreds of miles in diameter and hundreds of miles long. In other words, you look at the wire for the satellite, but you don't know how close it'll be to the wire, or how far along the wire it is.

"The difficulty of orbit determination lies in inaccurate data, noisy or dirty data, the fact that stations don't track the same satellite simultaneously, and the fact that some stations, the ones on islands, don't know their latitude and longitude accurately enough. You're working from marginal data."

Another problem is the placement of tracking ships. Syncom, the communications satellite, was to be launched in an equatorial orbit. Consequently it was necessary to establish a temporary tracking station as close to the equator as possible. NASA negotiated with Nigeria on the west coast of Africa for permission to put a tracking ship in one of their harbors, and ran into a ticklish question of political neutrality. Nigeria had to be convinced that Syncom was not a spy satellite, which NASA did by exhibiting its working parts. Nigeria and other neutral countries were afraid that United States tracking ships would invite Russian reprisals.

"In the early days," Siry said, "we only worried about a couple of things; apogee, perigee, and the inclination of the satellite's orbit to the earth. Now we have to worry about a lot of forces; the earth's pear-shape, radiation pressure, sunspots producing extra solar wind, lunar perturbation, solar perturbation, atmospheric bulge, and so on.

"When you launch a satellite there's always a two- or three-hour delay before you can determine its orbit. You need tracking data from at least three observations, and you rarely get more than one per orbit. Then you need time to process the data in a computer. This means you haven't got much to tell the press who want to know all about everything immediately."

But one NASA official said, "Don't let Joe Siry fool you. He outwits every computer at Goddard. He can read raw data and tell where to look for a satellite without using a computer."

The concept of launching spacecraft into an orbit around the earth seems to be far easier for most people to understand than the idea of launching a probe to land on a given crater on the moon, or to pass Mars in an encounter no more nor less than five thousand miles from the planet. How, they wonder, can you be accurate at a distance of 360 million miles?

Norman Haynes of the Jet Propulsion Laboratory, who plotted the trajectory for the Mariner Mars probe, says, "It really isn't all that difficult. It's like duck shooting, except that nothing's moving in a straight line. Imagine a duck flying in a circle. You shoot at him, but your bullet's going to fly a curved path, and when you shoot you're sitting there, going in a circle."

He chalked the inevitable diagram on the inevitable blackboard; two concentric circles representing the orbits of the earth and Mars around the sun. He placed the earth at three o'clock and Mars at three o'clock and drew a straight line between them. "You can't shoot this direct pattern from earth to Mars because it demands too much energy; it demands more power than a rocket vehicle can provide." He drew another Mars at twelve o'clock and chalked a curve from the earth to Mars in that position. "What you use is this pattern. You shoot from the earth, and add just enough energy to put the craft into an elliptical orbit around the sun. That orbit will intersect the orbit of Mars at precisely the same time that the planet is there. However, the launch vehicle is not this accurate, so a midcourse maneuver is required."

"Yes, but how do you know Mars will *be* there?"

"We use astronomical tables. Hundreds of years of astronomical research in celestial mechanics have gone into the compilation of an ephemeris of planetary orbits and positions."

"How accurately do you know Mars's position?"

"To fifty to one hundred kilometers; say thirty to sixty miles. We don't know planetary positions more precisely because of the uncertainty of the astronomical unit. We know the relative positions, but not the actual positions."

This requires some explanation. The astronomical unit is the mean distance of the earth from the sun, measured with geometric methods, gravitational methods, and using the speed of light. This distance cannot be measured more accurately than .003 seconds of arc. Three one-thousandths of a second would seem to be close enough, but by astronomical standards it's wide of the mark. The astronomical unit cannot be computed any more accurately than 93,004,000 miles, plus or minus 11,000 miles. That "plus or minus" is the joker.

The distances and positions of the planets are measured in astronomical units. They can't be measured in actual miles because you can't get a surveying team out there to do the job. They're measured by their reactions relative to each other and the sun, compared to the earth's reactions. We know, for example, that Saturn's behavior in its orbit indicates that it's 9½ astronomical units from the sun. Therefore its distance in miles is $93{,}004{,}000 \times 9.5 = 883{,}538{,}$-000 miles, *but* plus or minus an uncertainty of 104,500 miles. Since we're 100,000 miles off in the radius of its orbit, we're entitled to be a few hundred miles off in its position in the orbit.

Asked for the practical steps in computing trajectories, Haynes said, "You start with a book of conic trajectories. This is an encyclopedia of all possible trajectories to the moon, Mars, and Venus, worked out by theoretical astronomers in the past twenty years. First you assume that you will launch from the earth and fly an elliptical trajectory in which the sun is the only influence, and reach the target. This is the first rough assumption.

"Then you whittle all possibilities down to a few trajectories which will satisfy the constraints of the weight of the craft, the energy of the launch vehicle, and the flight time. There are many trajectories that would get you to Mars with a minimum of energy and a maximum of payload, but they would take so long that you run the risk of having your probe dead by the time it encounters the target. It's a general rule that gear can't live longer than six thousand hours or two hundred fifty days in space. Then you take your final conic trajectory and integrate it with a computer."

Integration is a method for solving partial differential equations, and this is the mathematical mystery that paralyzes the layman when he attempts to understand the space program. What, in God's name, are partial differential equations, and how are they solved, he asks. The trouble is, he usually asks a mathematician, and mathematicians are notorious for their inability to make themselves understood by the man in the street.

Let's take a simple example. You fire a gun at a target. The bullet must travel from the muzzle of the gun to the bull's-eye, but what factors are involved? The power of the explosive; the speed of the bullet; the mass or weight of the bullet; the air friction which slows it down; the wind current which can blow it off course; the attraction of the earth's gravity which will pull the bullet down; the revolution of the earth itself which will move the target. This seems farfetched, I know, but the truth is that it must be taken into account in long-range artillery fire. When a projectile is released from a gun, it becomes an independent contractor, no longer connected with the earth which is revolving underneath it.

Now, how do you plot the trajectory of the projectile? Each of these factors must be taken into account, so what you do is take the bullet at the moment it emerges from the gun and list all the influences; power, velocity, weight, friction, wind, gravity, and revolution. You add, subtract, multiply, and divide, and you know where the bullet will be as it comes out of the muzzle. But where will it be when it's an inch further along in its course? You repeat the same process, this time taking into account the results of the first computation. You repeat it over and over again, inch by inch, to the target, each time adding the factors produced by all previous results.

These computations can be put in equation form, and they're partial differential equations. They measure differences or changes affected by many interreacting variables. No mathematical formula has yet been devised for the solution of these equations, so they must be integrated, which is a tedious process of successive approximations. It can be done with pencil and paper, but it would take an infinity. The answer to this impasse is slave labor, performed by the computer which makes rapid integration possible. The computer, in essence, is merely a mathematical machine with an infinite capacity for arithmetic drudgery executed at speeds of a billionth of a second. It's a pity to destroy the Frankenstein legend, but a computer is nothing more than a high-speed hack. Two minutes on a computer equal fifty years of pencil work at eight hours a day in a forty-hour week.

Integrating a conic trajectory to Mars, the following variables must be taken into account: (1) the path of the craft;

(2) the gravitational attraction of the sun, the earth, the moon, Mars, Venus, Jupiter, and Saturn; (3) solar light pressure.

They are integrated step by step all the way to the target. Because these forces vary from day to day as the bodies and the spacecraft shift in their relationship to each other, the step sizes vary, depending on how close the craft is to the several forces acting on it. Near the earth you work out the trajectory second by second. Out in space it is only necessary to do it for every other day.

But the important thing to remember is that the forces acting on the craft are constantly changing: the planets are moving along in their orbits, and solar light pressure decreases as the probe travels farther and farther away from the sun. This is why I made the point that everything in space influences everything else. And this is why the trajectory of a probe is not a smooth curve, as some might think. The path it travels is constantly wobbling, as the various forces acting on the craft increase and decrease. This is another factor producing uncertainty about the final encounter with its target.

As if trajectories weren't complicated enough, you also have the problems of plane change and phase change. It will help you understand them if you'll remember a baseball game. If you've seen a game on television you must have seen camera shots from behind the pitcher or catcher, and noticed that a curve ball drops in its trajectory; it describes a curve down toward the ground. The plane of its trajectory is vertical.

The batter, on the other hand, is swinging his bat level with the ground. The plane of its trajectory is horizontal. His first constraint is to make sure that the plane of his swing will intersect the plane of the ball at some point. It's possible for the vertical plane of the ball to be so far to the left or right that the horizontal bat swing could never intersect it.

Any rendezvous in space has the identical problem. A probe launched to Mars must be launched on a trajectory whose plane will intersect with the plane of Mars's orbit. The rendezvous maneuver between two spacecraft in orbit around the earth in preparation for the Apollo mission to the moon also depends on this plane intersection.

Now back to the baseball example. The point where the plane of the curve ball intersects the plane of the bat swing is called the node. Not only must the batter be sure that the plane of his swing intersects the plane of the ball, but he must also time his swing so that bat and ball arrive at the node simultaneously. This is phasing, or phase change. It's not enough for the probe's trajectory to intersect with Mars's orbit; the craft must be phased so that it arrives at the node at the same moment that Mars arrives.

It was the requirements of phasing that brought about the development of the Parking Orbit concept. You must time your phase and initiate it at precisely the right moment. If you attempt to do this on the direct launch from earth, you only have one moment in every twenty-four hours. If you miss it because of delays in countdown, you have to wait a day before trying again, and it's possible that a day's delay might prove fatal to the entire mission. But if the craft is in a Parking Orbit, it's making a revolution around the earth every ninety minutes, which gives you the opportunity to phase every hour and a half.

These too are partial differential problems which are solved by computer integration. The Parking Orbit is tracked, and its elements are fed into a computer. The elements of the target, Venus, Mars, or a crater on the moon, are fed in, too. The computer does the dreary repetition which gives the moment-by-moment trajectories of target and craft, reveals the node point at which the planes will intersect, and indicates the moment at which the craft must be started toward that point. It also computes the amount of thrust that will be needed and the changes in course required.

The first computer tracking system for spacecraft was put together by Dr. Albert Hibbs and Dr. Fred Eimer at the Jet Propulsion Laboratory. Hibbs says, "When the first moon probes went up we had the problem of tracking and data, so we designed a system using the Goldstone eighty-five-foot antenna, teletype links for data, and a 704 computer.

"We used this on the Pioneer III shot [December, 1958] and it worked beautifully. The Pioneer III was the probe which revealed the existence of the second Van Allen belt. This was the first example of real-time orbit computing."

Real-time is computerese for control based on the reception of fresh data. Using an example from sports again, a football coach has spotters up in the stands watching the plays and telephoning their analyses and suggestions down to the bench. In a sense they're acting as computers, supplying data analysis on which the coach bases his decisions.

But suppose instead of being linked with the bench by telephone, the spotters were in direct communication with the players on the field. As they watched the plays develop and received the players' moment-by-moment reports . . . "I missed the block on the tight end because he's shifting to the right." They would be able to alter the players' actions through the plays on the basis of that information

. . . "Don't block the middle linebacker, Charlie. Take the tight end instead. He's shifting your way." This is real-time computing. The data that's received is immediately incorporated in the commands that are issued.

On manned missions computer tracking is crucial; after all, human lives depend on it. At least two computer systems are readied at the Goddard Space Flight Center, which is in control of all missions. The backup systems stand by in case the prime system fails. On John Glenn's flight the prime computer system was out for three minutes until the malfunction was located and repaired.

First the computers are checked out and programmed. Many people are awed by the golem implications of programming a computer, so let's dispel that immediately. The computer is a sort of universal arithmetic and logic shop; no matter what mathematical job you want done, you can always find the tools and procedures somewhere in the machine. The only problem is knowing where they're located and knowing how to instruct the machine to send the work to them. The programmer is the man (and often woman) who does this.

He writes his instructions in "compiler language," or "assembly language," and the act of instructing a computer is called coding a computer. Compiler language is a formal code using letters, punctuation, symbols and decimals. The machine has an automatic system for translating this code into the binary number commands that activate it.

Rather than use a space problem as an example of programming (it would take dozens of pages), let's use a simple problem in compound interest. In 1624 the Dutch swindled the Indians out of Manhattan Island for twenty-four dollars. If that money had been invested at 3½ per cent compound interest, how much would the Indians be worth today? Here is how the computer is coded:

```
1401 AUTOCODER
     ORG 500
     MLC + 1624, YEAR #1
     MLC + 24, DOLLAR #2
ONE  A + 1, YEAR
     MLC DOLLAR, TEMP #3
     M + 3.5, TEMP
     A + 5, TEMP -002
     A TEMP -003, DOLLAR
     C YEAR, + 1966
     BU ONE
     MCS DOLLAR, PRINT
     W
     H
     END
```

Now let's go through the program, step by step, and see what the code means:

1401 AUTOCODER This states the type of computer and the type of formal code to be used.

ORG 500 This is the code signal to begin the problem.

MLC + 1624, YEAR #1 Take the information that we're starting with the year 1624, and store it in Area 1.

MLC + 24, DOLLAR #2 Take the information that we're starting with $24, and store it in Area 2.

ONE A + *1, YEAR* The data is stored, and now the computation begins. The machine is instructed to add the number 1 to the year.

MLC DOLLAR, TEMP #3 Move the number of dollars to temporary location 3.

M + 3.5, *TEMP* There, multiply that number by the interest rate.

A + 5, *TEMP* –002 Add for rounding; that is, add enough to bring the interest to the nearest round number.

A TEMP –003, *DOLLAR* Add the year's interest to the total number of dollars.

C YEAR, + 1966 This is an automatic check. The computer is instructed to compare the year in Area 1, which is 1625, with 1966. The comparison can have one of two results.

BU ONE Branch unequal. That is, if the year in Area 1 is not equal to 1966, go back to the start of the computation at ONE A and repeat the process, or

MCS DOLLAR, PRINT When the C YEAR comparison shows that the year equals 1966, move to an area where you can print the result.

W Print.

H Halt.

END End the compilation.

Actually, the computer is merely repeating a simple process hundreds of times, and the most complicated mathematical problem can be reduced to a series of simple steps. Take multiplication as a crude example. We can multiply 1,234,567,890 by 1,234,567,890 using the arithmetic that was taught us in grammar school. But simple as this method is, it's too complicated for the idiot machine. The computer performs the multiplication by adding 1,234,567,-890 to itself 1,234,567,890 times.

In the Manhattan problem it would perform the multiplication in exactly the same way. It would add $24 to itself 35 times, and move the decimal point three places to the left to get 84 cents, the interest for one year at .035 (3½ per cent). Then it would add the 84 cents to the $24 and repeat the process. It would continue the repetitions 342 times, using over twelve thousand simple additions to solve the complex equation for compound interest.

The computer's electrons move the bits of data around in milliseconds (thousandths), microseconds (millionths), and nanoseconds (billionths). Some are even faster; so fast, in fact, that the ultimate limiting speed of light becomes an important factor in their operation. A kindergarten computation like the Manhattan problem would take a computer all of a second to complete. The answer, worked out with logarithms (no programmer would waste a computer's precious time on such foolishness), comes to approximately $3,088,213.

After the computers at the control center are prepared, the electronic equipment at the tracking stations is checked out. The display panels in the center reporting the status of electronic gear use green lights to indicate that equipment is operating properly, and red lights to indicate malfunction. Then a series of missions is simulated, and deliberate bugs are placed in the simulations to train flight controllers to handle them. These bugs are like fire drills. For example, medical telemetry will indicate that Astronaut X has become seriously ill while in orbit. How and where should he be brought down as quickly as possible? Should he be landed near any recovery ship, or do they have the time to wait until they can bring him down to a prime recovery ship with full hospital facilities?

After the simulations, the electronic equipment is checked again and readied for the actual flight. The point is, electronic equipment can be brought up to near-perfect performance, "peaked," but then it falls off and must be recalibrated. The idea is to bring the peak as close to the launch as possible.

"We hope to have a green board every time we go on a mission," Jim Donegan, chief of Data Operations at Goddard, says, "and so far it always has been. You lose face if your gear isn't green on shot day. You have a lot of explaining to do."

During the countdown the computers at Goddard have been prepared and have been driving zeros down to Cape Kennedy. This is the way a computer marks time. As I said before, you always send zeros if you've got nothing to say. Out on the launch pad at the Cape a wire is stretched under the rocket vehicle, two inches off the ground. It's called the "two-inch wire." At liftoff the two-inch wire starts the Goddard computer program, and it takes over the actual guidance of the craft into orbit, subject to the commands of the men who are running it. The computer digests data and makes suggestions; the men make the decisions.

The computers are operating on a real-time basis, but their real-time is approximately 2½ seconds behind event-time, obviously because radio and wire communications take time to travel. The computers monitor the launch to see if it's "nominal," which is the word engineers use for "according to plan." They send acquisition data to all tracking stations to tell them where to point their antennae to pick up the spacecraft, in other words "acquire" the spacecraft. Radar is locked on the craft and fed into the computers to give the craft's precise position every tenth of a second. The computers also operate real-time displays on giant graphs.

There are three critical areas for which you must have visual displays in the control center so that command decisions can be made quickly. These are the factors that influence the "Go" and "No Go" decisions, and they are: altitude of the craft, velocity of the craft, and the flight path angle. The flight path angle, indicated by the Greek letter gamma, tells whether the craft is rising or falling, relative to the surface of the earth.

During the countdown and the early stages of the mission, the pressure becomes tremendous. Don't let those posed pictures of neatly dressed men seated calmly at the control consoles fool you. The control center and the blockhouse become a mess of coffee containers, cigarette butts, and harassed technicians with frayed tempers. "It's Ulcer City," one of them muttered to me. "Like showbiz openings," another added.

But unlike the entertainment business, it's not a noisy display. My first launch experience was not with any of the OSO satellites, but with the AC-4 Centaur which was to be launched on a lunar orbit in preparation for the Apollo mission. The countdown began in the early hours of the morning, and the tension began to mount. Seven years of experiment and one hundred million dollars were at stake.

By eight o'clock in the morning the atmosphere was tight, but still no voice was raised. The illuminated display charts were ready; predicted flight path in red, velocity in amber, flight angle in black. Critical launch points such as booster engine cutoff and second stage cutoff were in green. The Goddard computers were driving zeros down to the Cape.

All lines between Goddard, the Cape, and the tracking stations were open, and there was casual, low-key conversation:

"Blockhouse Go."

"Pad Go."

"Stations Go."

"Board Go."

"Everything Go."

"T minus one minute ten seconds. Nine. Eight. Seven. Six ——"

"We don't need *every* second."

"Oh. Sorry."

Silence for a minute, and then the final count. "Five. Four. Three. Two. One. Zero. Ignition. Liftoff."

A white line on the flight path chart began to parallel the red line of the predicted path. Suddenly it stopped. A technician murmured, "Holy cow, she blew." An official opened the P.A. system communicating with all centers, and spoke in the impersonal voice of a croupier, "The AC-4 blew up on the pad."

The Centaur had lifted just enough to trigger the two-inch wire. Then one of her engines had faltered momentarily. The vehicle sagged back and jarred against the pad. Her casing cracked, and tons of liquid oxygen and hydrogen erupted into a four-hour inferno, trapping everybody in the blockhouse. There were no histrionics, but it was evident that everyone was deeply wounded by the disaster. A young man grunted, "Yeah, she was launched . . . in twenty different directions."

This is the way the world ends
This is the way the world ends
This is the way the world ends
Not with a bang but a whimper.

In America, for "whimper" read "wisecrack."

10
Test and Evaluation

AFTER eighteen months of experiment, trial and error, and assorted trail-breaking, the S-16 prototype and flight model were ready for Test and Evaluation. This is one of the most sensitive areas in satellite building. It's conducted with the rigid formality of a coronation ceremonial, and almost invariably creates hard feelings. John New, chief of the Test and Evaluation division at Goddard, says, "Designers are sore at Test and Evaluation. They claim you're always trying to make them fail. We're not doing that at all.

"We try to foster a climate in which a man doing a job can never escape from the responsibility of doing it right. We try to inject objectivity into Test and Evaluation, but we also try to inject helpfulness. We're the conscience of the project. It's a damnable business because we're always dealing with failures, and people don't like to talk about their failures."

The satellite tests are conducted in three stages. The first is integration and checkout, called the pre-launch environment test. The satellite is integrated and checked as a working system. The experiment packages are fitted into the body, and all of the mechanical and electrical systems are operated and checked to make sure they're functioning properly together. This is a Castilian ceremony in itself. The experiments are delivered to the prime contractor, and the following tests take place:

1. Electrical Interface. This is to see whether pieces of electrical equipment of the experiments interfere with each other and the operation of the satellite. Suppose you have a magnetometer experiment to map the earth's magnetic field, and an experiment using a photomultiplier. The magnetometer uses magnetic compass arrangements to do its work; the photomultiplier uses huge quantities of voltage. That voltage may induce a magnetic field which will betray the magnetometer into measuring the field of the photomultiplier rather than that of the earth. The experiments must be so placed that they will not interfere with each other.

2. Mechanical Interface. This is to see whether there is any mechanical interference between the experiments and the satellite. S-16 had one problem that was particularly annoying. The wheel had miniature barn doors which opened and closed on experiments. They were necessary in order to prevent gas from filming the optical systems during launch, and to act as light-baffles. But they upset the balance of the satellite as they swung. Bob Mattingly of Goddard says, "They had to be counterpoised with massive weights, and this was a paradox. Here they were so worried about weight that they shifted to magnesium for structural parts, and yet they were adding counterweights."

3. Preliminary Test Specifications. The Test and Evalu-

ation specialists sit down and decide what they're going to test for.

4. Preliminary Test Procedures. Having decided what they're going to test for, they decide how to go about it.

5. Prototype Bench Test for Interface Compliance. This is done in the presence of the experimenters, who are never any help. John New says, "Whenever there's a failure, the designer claims you tested it wrong."

6. Final Test Procedures. This is a repetition of the preceding prototype bench tests in the event that they revealed weaknesses which necessitated redesigning the gear. The redesign must be tested.

7. Flight Experiment Delivery. The examiners say, "We don't consider the flight experiment has been delivered until its prototype has passed all acceptance tests." The flight model is subjected to the same tests, but far less strenuously so as not to fatigue it.

The Ball Brothers *Comprehensive Acceptance Test Procedure* book is one hundred twenty pages long. It breaks the tests down into a step-by-step process, spelling everything out meticulously. Here is the ritual for the testing of a solar X-ray experiment. You'll be able to understand some of the items; the rest don't matter, except as an illumination of the infinite pains that go into the birth of a satellite.

3.5.5 SOLAR X-RAY EXPERIMENT

3.5.5.1 Special Precautions

The special precautions as stated in BBRC Experiment Handling Document No. P15973 have been adhered to and are carried out as discrete operational steps in the following procedure. It is mandatory that special care be taken to insure that the environmental pressure at no time exceeds normal atmospheric pressure. Otherwise, severe damage might occur to the ion gauge window.

3.5.5.2 Test Equipment

Verify operation and/or availability of the following:

a. Laboratory Ground Station
b. Ground Station Ampex Tape Recorder
c. Computer, Control Data Model 160-A
d. Sun Gun
e. Radiation Source Fe^{55}

3.5.5.3 Test Methods

a. Digital data from this experiment are read out on word 23 of the main frame.
b. Load Ampex tape recorder for Experiment input.
c. Load the computer program for the Experiment print and evaluation.
d. Patch out Experiment data words on ground station de-commutator patch board.
e. Remove the protective covers on the instrument.

3.5.5.3.1 Turn On Procedure

Turn on Satellite Control Console.

Start Ampex tape recorder.

Set Computer to "Run" condition.

Computer printout should read all zero's and in low sensitivity.

Command Wheel 0310 (Experiment on).

First three (3) readouts after turn-on should be 127's.

3.5.5.3.2 Sun Pulse Indication

Activate Sun gun and direct light beam at Sun sensor.

Sun pulse indication should appear on computer print-out.
Deactivate Sun gun.

3.5.5.3.3. Calibration Check
A calibration readout occurs every 512 readouts after the initial calibration occurs.
Calibration value is 109 plus or minus 1 counts.

3.5.5.3.4 Ion Chamber Check
Position radiation source flush with rim panel and centered on ion chamber entrance.
Data readout is 19, 22, or 23.
Maintain the source position until:
Calibration occurs,
Low-range readout occurs,
and high-range readout occurs.
Remove source.
Data readout is 0, 1, or 3.
Operate in this condition long enough for three (3) calibrates to occur.
Monitor sub-commutator words 2 and 27.

3.5.5.3.5 Night Mode Check
Command Wheel 0605.
Data readout should be all zeros.

3.5.5.3.6 Day Cycle Check
Command Wheel 0509
First three (3) readouts after cycling into Day are 127's.

3.5.5.3.6 Shut Down
Monitor sub-commutator channels 2 and 27.

Command Wheel 0905 (Experiment off).
Monitor print-out for termination of operation.
Shut down Computer.
Shut down tape recorder.
Re-cover the Sun sensor and ion chamber entrance.

I like that last touch. It really should be followed by "Sweep up all dust and deposit in step-can," but of course there is no dust in a satellite factory.

After the prelaunch integration and check out, the launch environment tests begin. When a launch takes place, vehicle and payload are subjected to the frightful stresses of vibration and acceleration for sustained periods; they're shoved up into space and shaken and rattled like dice in a birdcage. Everything must be rugged enough to withstand this mauling.

The spacecraft is subjected to the forces of vibration, shock, and acceleration in the Test and Evaluation laboratory. Much of the launch vibration is acoustical, the same acoustical vibration which legend claims enables a tenor to break a glass with a high note. Actually, no singer has ever been able to do this, but a launch certainly can. Vibrations and accelerations are created to simulate the total frequency range encountered during a launch.

During these tests the systems in the satellite that will be used during the launch are operated at their nominal working level. They are monitored for malfunctions, and if one is located, the tests stop until it's corrected. Then the tests are continued, but John New says, "Sometimes you reach a point of test and fix, test and fix, test and fix, where it would be more profitable on this particular shot with this particular craft to take a risk. Ultimately it boils down to a game of confidence and economy. For instance, with sounding rockets, which cost around fifty grand, you test at a minimum because it costs as much to test it as to make it. So you say, 'To hell with it. Don't test it, launch it.' "

Next, the space environment tests are conducted to check resistance to hard vacuum and extreme temperatures. The satellite prototype is placed in a thermal-vacuum chamber, which is the size of a large boiler, and looks rather ominous with its clutter of plumbing and wiring. One of the NASA scientists, a refugee from Nazi Germany, once passed a thermal-vacuum chamber and muttered, "Will accommodate twenty Jews."

The satellite is operated by remote control under varying conditions of vacuum and high and low temperatures. The temperatures range from -65 degrees centigrade to 100 degrees centigrade. Vacuums of 1×10^{-9} millimeters of mercury are produced. That is, the atmospheric pressure is pumped down so low that it will only raise the mercury column in a barometer .000,000,000,1 millimeters, or .000,000,000,039 inches. This simulates the conditions existing in space at an altitude of four hundred miles. Normal sea-level atmospheric pressure raises the mercury column around 1016 millimeters, or thirty inches.

Hard vacuum is the ogre of space, and it's almost impossible to reproduce on earth. The average chamber can be exhausted to 10^{-7} millimeters of mercury. Exceptional chambers can be pumped out to 10^{-9} (incidentally, these figures are read as "ten-to-the-minus-nine"). Experimental chambers can get down to 10^{-12}, but this is very rare. They can't do much testing in it because at that vacuum everything contaminates the chamber. Materials outgas, constantly producing molecules. It's almost an experiment in itself to produce an uncontaminated vacuum of 10^{-12} millimeters of mercury.

The trouble is, three hundred miles out in space is the lowest orbit for a scientific satellite, and at that altitude the vacuum is of the order of 10^{-9}. At five hundred miles out, the vacuum is 10^{-11}, and things begin to happen at 10^{-11} that don't happen at 10^{-9}; but it's virtually impossible to produce these conditions in a vacuum chamber, so you never really know what's going to happen to the satellite.

Speaking of the philosophy of Test and Evaluation, John New says, "When something fails in space, we can only talk to it through the radio system. You make it obey a series of built-in responses to commands. This means you have to pre-program every possible failure. Each spacecraft is almost human. It has its own idiosyncrasies, and you learn these when you test.

"It's awfully hard to make an engineer keep his hands off a piece of equipment that's out of adjustment, but you can't do this in space. You put a device in the vacuum chamber, it goes wrong, and the engineer says, 'Just let me get at it for a minute and I can fix it.' You have to make him realize that he can't do this when it's in orbit. That's why the vacuum chamber has to have thick walls, to keep those mad experimenters out."

Jim Kupperian says, "We have no problem finding out what's wrong with a satellite when it's in orbit. We can always find out, but we can't do anything about it. Very often all it needs is a kick, but you can't get up there and kick it."

And yet sometimes it is possible to kick the satellite. Bill Scull and Tom Ragland of Goddard did this to OGO, the Orbiting Geophysical Observatory. OGO was designed to face the earth constantly while it was in orbit, and had an earth sensor to keep it locked on its target. OGO also had extended booms carrying instruments. One of the booms was jammed by the jolting of the launch, and did not extend fully. It hung down alongside the satellite, and the idiot sensor locked on the boom instead of the earth. As a result, the satellite went into a slow spin, chasing its own boom.

This was bad, but not a complete disaster; it was still possible for the satellite to acquire some data. Unfortunately the spin produced something far more serious. OGO had solar panels to charge the batteries, and the panels were controlled by a switch to keep them facing the sun. Since OGO was spinning once every twelve seconds, the switch was attempting to adjust to the sun every twelve seconds, something it had not been made to do. After 100,000 on-off operations, the switch stuck. This meant that the spinning solar panels could never face the sun long enough to charge the batteries, and the satellite power began to dwindle down to the death point.

Scull and Ragland figured they had an outside chance to give the satellite a swift kick in the pants. As the solar panels revolved with OGO they were facing toward and facing away from the sun. When they faced away they produced no current at all. When they faced the sun directly, they produced fifty volts. When they were oblique to the sun they produced any voltage between those two extremes, depending on their position.

The outside chance was this: if the batteries were disconnected from the solar panels at the right moment, the full voltage would feed into the entire satellite system, and might jolt the switch back into action. On the other hand, it might also destroy the experiments which OGO was carrying.

They timed the spin of the satellite to the split second, selected the moment when the panels were producing ten volts of electricity, sent the disconnect command, and gave OGO a ten-volt shock. Nothing happened. They waited and sent another command at twenty volts. Again nothing. They tried a third time and kicked the satellite with forty volts. The shock reactivated the switch and, *mirabile dictu,* did not destroy the experiments.

"And that's the real importance of test chambers," New says. "They train people to keep their hands off and work at a distance. They train them to look ahead, pre-plant, and prepare for all possible circumstances. We've learned to test every part of the system, including the people. People are a part of a project that's often overlooked. The human parts are tough. They have feelings and get mad, and, unlike satellites, they talk back."

11

The Launch of OSO

HERE is a summary of the final sequence of tests which S-16 (OSO) underwent before launch. Note how it was inspected and tested comprehensively after each individual checkout.

PRE-ENVIRONMENTAL SYSTEMS CHECK

Initial Comprehensive Test

Spacecraft Monitoring System Checkout and Calibration

Post Integration Inspection

Balance

Alignment Check

Integrated Comprehensive

Pre-Flight Checkout

VIBRATION TESTING

Z-axis Vibration

Covers-On Inspection

Integrated Comprehensive

X-axis Vibration
Covers-On Inspection
Quick Look Functional Checks
Y-axis Vibration
Covers-On Inspection
Integrated Comprehensive
Supplemental Tests (Pointing, Boresight)

THERMAL VACUUM TESTING

Main Battery Deep Discharge
Pre-flight Checkout
Spacecraft Setup in Vacuum Chamber
Pump down and Launch Sequences
Hot Run: 3 days at 25° C.
Supplementary Run at 25° C.
Temperature Transition
Cold run: 3 days at 0° C.
Supplementary 25° C. Run
Chamber Bleed Up

PRE-SHIPMENT PREPARATIONS

Pre-shipment Comprehensive
Monitoring System Checkout
Current Measurements
Main Battery Deep Discharge
Pre-shipment Button-up

In February, 1962, the S-16 flight model was buttoned up and shipped to Cape Canaveral. Contrary to previous estimates, it had taken over two years to build, and cost five million dollars so far. The launch would cost an additional two and a half million dollars. The launch vehicle was a three-stage Thor-Delta rocket, built by Douglas Aircraft. S-16, accompanied by technicians from BBRC, was sent to the Douglas hanger at the Cape. The rocket contractor is in charge of the launch. John Lindsay was there with the other experimenters and the NASA experts to watch the final Terminal-3 comprehensive tests, and the mating of the payload to the third-stage X-248 engine.

The satellite, protected from contamination by a polyethylene bag, was removed from the handling can. It was hoisted on top of the X-248 engine, clamped into place, and bolted. Then the ordnance collar was attached. This collar has explosive bolts and springs to separate the final stage from the payload at the completion of the boost. The polyethylene bag was raised to permit the alignment of the satellite and the third stage, and then the craft was purged of dust and contamination with pure nitrogen gas.

The satellite and the fueled third stage were then carefully moved to the spin-balance jig, a sort of giant lathe, and checked for perfect balance in all positions. This is essential to achieve an accurate trajectory in the launch. Small weights were inserted into the payload in various positions to accomplish this, and allowance had been made for this final adjustment. Then the craft waited its turn in the launch schedule, which came on March 6.

S-16 was to be injected into orbit one thousand miles downrange from the Cape exactly at noon. This meant that the plane of its orbit would always be on a direct line with the sun, requiring a minimum of pointing control. Consequently, the launch was scheduled for 11:50 A.M. In other words, this was a phasing maneuver, and 11:50 A.M. was the one moment of the day during which they could bring it off.

"We counted down," Lindsay said, "and pushed the launch button. Nothing happened. The thing just sat there on the pad. Later we found out what went wrong. The pressure in the liquid-oxygen tank hadn't had time enough to build up. I believe if they'd pushed the button again, it would have lifted off. Instead we waited until the next day."

(Lindsay was using a figure of speech when he spoke of "pushing the button." You don't push a button to launch spacecraft; the entire procedure is programmed into a computer which executes it, step by step.)

On March 7, S-16 was launched successfully and became OSO-I, but Lindsay's headaches were just beginning. "In orbit we had a hell of a situation," he drawled. "I think the word is, we goofed. We'd hoped that the air drag would slow OSO down from the ballistic spin of the launch, and then we could use the gas bottles to regulate it. The question had come up of what would happen if it spun faster, but it was too late to add a de-spin system. Sure enough, OSO-I began whirling like a spinwheel. The spin-up disrupted the data, and the pointing control couldn't acquire the sun."

That meant that the solar array wasn't receiving enough light from the sun to generate full electric power. After a time, the spin rate slowly reduced so that OSO could acquire the sun again, but although the sun sensor and pointing control were working perfectly, they could no longer help because the solar array was being destroyed by the radiation of the Starfish shot.

This was the highly controversial armed forces experiment of exploding a nuclear bomb at high altitude, and many scientists are still raising hell about it. The Starfish bomb exploded with a power of 1.4 megatons 250 miles above Johnston Island in the Pacific on the night of July 9, 1962. It was a spectacular blast, producing auroras three thousand miles away, disrupting radio broadcasting, shocking the earth's magnetic field into hysterical oscillations, and spreading an artificial radiation belt around the earth which wiped out many satellites.

But the freak disaster that did the most damage to OSO-I could hardly be called a goof. As I mentioned before, commands were sent to the satellite by a rather primitive system of radio tone signals which vibrated reeds that opened and closed relays. The mission team discovered, to its amazement and horror, that every time OSO flew over North Africa it was receiving commands from nowhere that threw its tape recorders into a frenzy. They went into a constant stop-start-stop-start chatter.

No one could figure out where this unknown voice was coming from. Hogarth suggested that the radio tone might be a beat produced by the accidental combination of the broadcasts from two North African radio stations. Fred Dolder of BBRC disagreed. He said, "These stations don't broadcast twenty-four hours a day, and it made no difference, day or night, we got screwed up over North Africa." Lindsay thought that the air tower of a private airfield might have been responsible. It was also suggested that perhaps French military installations were producing the alien commands.

No matter what the source was, the OSO-I tape recorders were throwing fits on every pass over North Africa, and they hadn't been built to withstand that. NASA flew a special tracking team to an island in the Mediterranean. Every time the satellite flew over, the team broadcast a continuing command to it to keep its tape recorders going, but by then it was too late. The recorders were exhausted and could no longer function. This meant that the satellite could no longer store data during its orbit and dump it on command. It could only deliver the data it happened to be acquiring during its pass over a tracking station, that is, real-time data.

In effect, OSO-I had performed well for its first thousand orbits, measuring solar phenomena through three full revolutions of the sun. Then it slowly came unglued, and limped along for another year, occasionally supplying useful data. Asked about the results of the experiments, Lindsay said, "The X-ray measurements revealed that the flux from the sun varied with the rotation of the sun. High-energy lines like Iron fifteen [Fe_{15}] and Iron sixteen [Fe_{16}] varied most, almost by four hundred per cent.

"Iron fifteen means fourteen electrons have been stripped off, leaving you looking at the fifteenth. This means a lot of energy was used to strip them off. This gave indications of what regions of the sun emit particular radiation. Also we were able to correlate the temperature of the upper atmosphere with flux in radiation, and showed that the temperature of the upper atmosphere is caused by the sun's ultraviolet radiation."

On the gamma-ray measurements, Lindsay said, "Gee, they were lousy experiments. None of them came up with a positive answer. It was rough because radiation belt particles form a secondary background of noise. Gamma ray experiments have been notably unsuccessful because of this background noise."

On the correlation of X-ray bursts and radio bursts, they discovered that both came from the explosive phase of sun flares. Lindsay didn't like to think about the dust particle detector. "Damn! I'd forget about that one if I were you. I don't know if they ever got any results from that." He was also unhappy about the solar radiation flux detector. "It was a lousy experiment."

The measurement of solar radiation in the Lyman alpha and Lyman beta wavebands disclosed a 7 per cent variation in the solar flux, but the results were not very firm. The University of Rochester's measurement of high-energy gamma-ray activity didn't give very good results either, and it was decided to try it again.

The University of California's investigation of the inner Van Allen belt discovered "warm spots" or "hot spots" in the belt in which the particle density was stronger than that of surrounding neighborhoods. These warm spots are over Hawaii, Australia, and the South Pacific, west of South America. It's still not known what causes them. The experiment also recorded good data on the decay of the artificial Starfish radiation belt.

Bill Hess's neutron monitor found less than one per cent variation in the count of neutrons on the dark side of the earth and the sun side. Since one per cent was the limit of the accuracy of his monitor, this meant that he found no effects at all. "In other words," Hess said, "the same number of neutrons seem to be coming in all over the earth from all directions at the same time. This was surprising because they should show a preference as a result of the sun.

"Now our problem is: is something disturbing this expected preferential distribution and randomly scattering the neutrons, or will it be necessary to work out a new mathematical model for particle diffusion?"

Despite the fact that the OSO-I results had been in no way spectacular, NASA was encouraged enough to enlarge the project. Lindsay's years of pleading and persuasion paid off, and six future missions were planned. The working title of S-17 was changed to OSO-B, and OSO-C through OSO-H were scheduled. This meant that the pressures on Lindsay would be quintupled, but he welcomed them. He felt that a scientist's productive life lies between the ages of thirty and fifty, and he was raging to achieve recognition while he still had time.

In honor of his success, Lindsay turned OSO-I on for a short time to celebrate its second anniversary. It was still emitting a plaintive warble. Lindsay's poker face betrayed no sign of what he was feeling; what everyone who has ever worked on a satellite feels. As one engineer put it, "A pass is like a giant Fourth of July celebration. When that thing comes beeping over the gas station you know that a piece of you is out there in space."

12

The Second OSO

LONG before OSO-I was flown, Hogarth had started work on S-17 and the backup S-57, which were subsequently lettered OSO-B and OSO-C. Vital changes were introduced into the OSO-B; a de-spin system, for one, and an accident-proof radio command system, for another. More about that later. The specifications for OSO-B were circularized in the NASA Blue Book and experiments were solicited. In April, 1961, eight experiments for OSO-B were approved by the Solar Physics subcommittee and duly passed by the Steering Committee. They were:

POINTED

Ultraviolet Spectrometer — Spectroheliograph 500 to 1500 A.U. — Harvard College Observatory

This was a refinement of the OSO-I uv measurements. That experiment had looked at the entire sun. It got flux measurements, but not special regional measurements. This experiment could look at spectra from small areas and tell how large the source was.

NASA was very happy to welcome powerful and influential Harvard aboard. It was a status achievement in the scientific community.

Monitor solar X-ray bursts: 2 to 8 A.U., 8 to 20 A.U., and 44 to 60 A.U., and map X-ray sources—NRL [Naval Research Laboratory]

This was Dr. Chubb's experiment and was actually several simultaneous measurements intended to answer an interesting question: Were there X-ray events on the sun that did not have any corresponding optical events? Could there be an X-ray flare without an optical flare? Chubb hoped to make his measurements with Geiger counters.

White Light Coronagraph—Spectroheliograph solar scan in Lyman alpha 1216 A.U., Helium I-584 A.U., and the Helium II-304 A.U. lines—NRL

This, too, was several experiments in one. It was Dr. Tousey's package and hoped to measure the energy, distribution and polarization of the solar corona, and measure ultraviolet energy at three levels; 304 A.U., 388 A.U., and 1216 A.U. Tousey was using photomultipliers along with the coronagraph.

The coronagraph was developed by Bernard Lyot in 1930 to photograph the solar corona which usually can be seen only during a total eclipse. Lyot produced an artificial eclipse by masking the sun with an opaque disc, but had to take extraordinary measures to reduce the scattered light in the lens system of his telescope to a minimum.

The advantage of flying a coronagraph in a satellite is

that you don't have to contend with the atmospheric scattering of light, or shimmer and scintillation effects out in space. This was an experiment to see if the coronagraph would work.

Both Chubb and Tousey were sharing a Raster Scan Mode to look at the sun. ("Mode" is merely the engineer's fancy word for method.) Your TV tube uses a raster scan, which is what produces the horizontal lines on the screen. A beam of electrons sweeps back and forth across the inner face of the tube from top to bottom, producing an image on the phosphorescent face. The raster scan sweeps across the sun's face in exactly the same way. The advantage is that you can select extremely small areas for examination.

WHEEL

Monitor intensity and direction of polarized light from interplanetary space — University of Minnesota

Zodiacal light (pronounced zo-*dye*-a-cal) is a phenomenon seen best during March evenings and September mornings. It's a faint wedge of light extending up into the sky from the eastern horizon just before dawn, and from the western horizon just after sunset.

Zodiacal light is scattered light, but nobody knows what the scattering medium is. Some people think it might be dust. Measurements have indicated that the light may be polarized, that is, its waves vibrate in one particular direction rather than in all directions. This would indicate nonspherical dust in space. Other people think the polarization may take place in the earth's atmosphere.

Dr. Ed Ney of the University of Minnesota was investigating this phenomenon, and also the earth's airglow layer.

We don't usually see the airglow at night because of its low contrast. Try the experiment of looking at a clump of trees on a moonless night. After your eyes accommodate to the darkness, you'll see the trees silhouetted against the sky. One tenth of the backlight that shows up the trees comes from the stars; nine tenths is the airglow.

The airglow phenomenon had been noted for many years, but nothing much was done by way of investigation, particularly of the fact that on some nights in some areas it's extremely bright. This was the first systematic examination of the puzzle.

Measure arrival direction and energies of primary cosmic gamma rays: 100 Mev to 1 Bev — University of New Mexico

This was an attempt to gather information about one of the most perplexing enigmas of cosmology. How are cosmic rays born, and where do they come from? Are they generated within our own galaxy, or do they come to us through extra-galactic space from other galaxies?

Detect gamma rays and analyze their energy spectrum: 0.1 to 0.7 Mev — GSFC [Goddard Space Flight Center]

This was an improved version of the original Goddard experiment on OSO-I.

Ultraviolet stellar and nebular Spectrophotometer: 1300 to 2600 A.U. — GSFC

This was Dr. Hallam's experiment and it had two objectives. Some rocket shots had indicated that there was a difference between the theoretical and the measured ultraviolet flux in the emissions from stars. Hallam was checking this. He was also looking for data to be used in programming the proposed Orbiting Astronomical Observatory (OAO). He was scouting for the mission to save OAO the trouble of hunting for interesting objects to observe when it was in space.

Measurement of thermal-radiation characteristics of surfaces to determine emissivity stability of spacecraft temperature-control coatings — Ames Research Center

A continuation of the OSO-I technological experiments. Ames is a bulldog for tenacity.

Hogarth brought to the mission his crisp administrative efficiency. "I had to put management into OSO. I had to take a collection of private individuals and turn them into a corporation. This took a lot of persuasion and argument and force. We're in constant combat twenty-four hours a day, with Mother Nature on the one hand and with people on the other. These scientific types are really very unscientific. They do things the way a woman does things, on impulse and intuition."

Perhaps. But the truth is that Hogarth himself very often leaped to decisions by intuition. Lindsay would spot this, and since John loved doing puzzles . . . in fact he usually turned scientific problems into puzzles before he solved them . . . he would make a game of puzzling out the factors that had led to Hoge's decision. They both enjoyed it very much.

"Ball Brothers Research Corporation originally started as a college group," Hogarth went on (you may remember that they were hired from the faculty of the University of Colorado), "and they had the same resistance to organization, too. They felt it was some sort of government interference. It was a long struggle to make them all understand the meaning of 'accountability.' You can't just do something. You must be prepared at all times to account for what you've done and why you did it."

The first thing that Hogarth did was go over the list of experiments with Lindsay and draft a budget for OSO-B in terms of power requirements for day and night operations, weight limitations, weight balance, number of commands required, volume of space available, and so on. Then he called a meeting at Boulder for the experimenters, to explore the problems of fitting the experiments and the craft together.

Hogarth had seen Lindsay forced to scratch around the last minute to replace the University of Colorado experiment on OSO-I, so he insisted on a prototype, flight experiment, and flight spare for every package. He warned the experimenters not to deviate between the three (there's always a strong tendency to do this), set an arbitary date for the delivery of prototypes and flight experiments, and sent them home to think it over. "They went away glassy-eyed, upped their estimates, and everything went into routine crisis."

Hogarth was now working full time on the OSO mission. He was handling technical problems and scrapping with BBRC over them. "They were using too many castings because they were committed to the design. I was niggling them to switch to forgings or to machine the parts out of solid materials." He had a battle with them over bearings. Hogarth demanded the reasons and evidence for their decision to use certain bearings. "They had no records from S-16 and didn't see any reason why they should produce any.

S-17 was the first methodical job of satellite-building with records of everything." But he wasn't endearing himself to people while he was putting method into the mission.

"There are tricky difficulties with contractors. How do they deploy their staffs? If they charge for full-time services of an engineer who is also working on another mission, should you pay it? But would you know? How do you find out? Do you pay for two weeks of a man's work who was doing something which you think should have taken two days? If the staff is idle between missions, do you pay for them to avoid losing them?"

Asked why his administration had such an uphill struggle, Hogarth said, "Scientists hate NASA the way foreign countries hate the United States. NASA is handing out huge sums of money, and people usually hate their benefactors. Plus the fact that NASA imposes rules and scheduling; it's playing father, and that's another reason why it's hated.

"I don't believe we encountered any lasting hostility from scientists. If we ran into hostility at all, it was out in Boulder. The problem there was partly that some of the group were leaving academic freedom for the first time, and partly a sort of dislike of government.

"Their people were completely dependent on federal spending, a thing to which they had always been opposed. Their reaction to this conflict was essentially one of, 'Please send check, and stay out!' And that, of course, was something that we could not do when we were accountable for the spending of large sums of public money."

Hogarth was monitoring craft and experiment schedules. "The object of NASA is to bring the experimenter to the contractor at exactly the right time so there will be no delays. The experimenter must meet the contractor's milestones." He was distributing NASA funds to the experimenters to finance their packages. "One of them was too modest. All he asked me for was forty thousand dollars. I knew it wasn't enough but sent it anyway. Sure enough, he sneaked around later and asked for another hundred and sixty thousand." Hogarth was doing organizational work both at NASA and at the contractors'. "And I spent a lot of time answering damn fool questions from higher up."

Most of the experimenters subcontracted the work of building their packages. Harvard, however, insisted on building the spectrophotometer experiment itself. Hogarth, keenly watchdogging the schedule, and angering almost everybody with his insistence that deadlines be met, discovered that Harvard was dangerously late. "A year after the first experimenters' meeting they didn't even have a shopping list drawn up for components. Although some experimenters are humble, like that forty-thousand-dollar character, others want to set up a tremendous organization. Harvard was making a big production, but their scientists were vague about the steps they were taking to get their experiment ready."

Fully aware that he was taking on a powerful opponent — "When you step on these people's toes they don't complain to their congressman, they go straight to the White House." — Hogarth employed cautious strategy. He waited very carefully until Harvard was really in trouble. Then he went up to Cambridge and, fully aware that it didn't exist, asked for their shopping list with dates. "They didn't have one, and didn't know how to put one together. They finally had to face the fact that they'd be late, and they were shaken."

Hogarth then took the experimenters out to lunch and soothed them. He pointed out, very gently, that building a million-dollar instrument package was big business, and suggested that they might be too busy with other campus affairs to handle it efficiently. Harvard was so abashed that they finally agreed to use Pert, and the entire scientific community across the country went into shock.

Pert is the acronym for Program Evaluation and Review Technique, and the word is used both as a noun and a verb. Pert was developed by management efficiency experts at the request of Admiral Rickover. The Navy was the first organization to use Pert or, to accustom you to the acronym as a verb, the first to pert a project.

Pert is used to integrate the thousands of steps involved in the schedule of a big project, and it operates something like this: First you draw up a list of all the steps (Pert analysts call them "events") that must take place in order to complete the project. This is your input. As an example, let's use the project of hanging a picture on a wall.

INPUT

Hammer
Picture wire
Screw eyes
Picture hook
Nail for hook
Screws attached to frame
Wire threaded through screws
Nail put in hook
Select place for hook
Nail hook to wall

Hang picture
Adjust wire for height
Level picture

Next, the events are placed in their proper sequence or logic.

LOGIC

1. Select place for hook
2. Get picture hook
3. Get nail for hook
4. Put nail in hook
5. Get hammer
6. Hammer nail and hook into wall.
7. Get screw eyes
8. Put screw eyes into frame —

Of what? Certainly the technique seems absurd for a simple thing like hanging a picture on a wall, but even this Pert analysis has revealed a mistake in the Input. Nowhere in the list of events is there any mention of procuring the picture which was to be hung. It was taken for granted.

But you can't take anything for granted when thousands of events on different levels and in different branches must be sequenced, coordinated, and timed to avoid delay. Suppose you're a construction company building a hospital. When do you order steel, concrete, bricks, and other materials? If they arrive before they're needed they must be stored, and you've tied up capital unnecessarily. If they arrive late, your workmen have been idle, and your labor costs go up.

Pert charts are drawn as vast networks of squares and

connecting lines. Each square represents a single event which must take place. The lines or arrows represent the time that will be required to complete each event, estimated in weeks and tenths of weeks, and the figures are written above the arrows.

These figures are periodically fed into a computer which integrates them and then tells you how far behind you are in your schedule, from baseline to finish. This is called the Negative Slack. If you fall too far behind, the computer will do an analysis and tell you which event or events in the network are responsible. Then you can speed the work up in that area by shifting technicians and work schedules.

There was the case of the New York builder who was unhappy about expensive delays in the completion of his housing project. He bought a Pert analysis of the construction system he was using in order to discover what lapses were costing him so much money. He was made even more unhappy when the computer revealed that he himself was producing the Negative Slack through his failure to decide on what color brick to use.

What the Pert analysts watch most carefully is what they call the "Critical Path." This is the one sequence of events, among many, which they judge may be the most difficult, and the most apt to delay the final completion of the job. It often proves to be the longest path in the network, but length isn't the only factor. There was a California aircraft company subcontracting the construction of a missile component. They were worrying about everything except the one crucial part, which Pert analysis revealed. That was a tungsten nut that held the entire component together, and its procurement was the Critical Path.

The Pert charts are enormous, measuring three feet by six

feet. A prime contractor may be working with fifteen charts, or networks, each containing two hundred events. Experimenters usually have one network for each experiment, averaging between two hundred and two hundred and fifty events. They are updated every two weeks, and reports are made on the completion of each path. The estimated time for the completion of each event is revised as the work progresses. Almost invariably it's an upward revision.

Hogarth had taken a leaf from Lindsay's book — never let your right hand know what your left hand is doing — and hadn't told Lindsay about his plan to pert Harvard. "We then announced it, and John got wild because he was afraid that his experiment would be perted, too. All the other scientists at Goddard felt the same way, and they brought the roof down.

"Scientists hate Pert, but they're forced to use it, and it's changed them from academicians to the man outside. As a matter of fact, you find that the old-time scientists were actually perting their work before the study was developed. They worked methodically and in sequence."

But Hogarth understood the antipathy. "The danger is that some people go overboard with Pert and turn everything into a Pert exercise. The question of having Pert is like asking whether you should have a bridle on a horse. If you handle the bridle unsympathetically, you can pull a horse over backwards."

However, once Harvard was maneuvered into Pert, Hogarth was able to pert everybody else. "I said to them, 'If Harvard did it, why shouldn't you?' They replied, 'Oh? Harvard did it? Oh well, all right.' And when Harvard admitted that it was the best thing that ever happened to them, even the scientists at Goddard stopped fighting it.

These college chaps have to be pressed. They're inherently opposed to any sort of organization."

Unfortunately this is true. The NASA operation is not classified, but it is carefully protected. Everyone, from the most distinguished visiting director on down, must wear an identification tag on campus. But the NASA security guards often must wrestle with visiting scientists who refuse to wear tags because they claim it's an infringement of academic freedom.

13

NASA in Full Stride

By the time OSO-B was getting under way in late 1961, NASA was in full stride, and many other scientific satellites and probes were being developed in parallel with OSO. At the Jet Propulsion Laboratory they were sweating out the ordeal of the Ranger program. Nothing seemed to go right, and there were periodic upheavals.

Rangers I and II were started in the middle of 1960. The payloads were cislunar experiments: magnetometer, ion chamber, particles and fields measurements, and others, mounted on a sort of oil derrick frame. Both craft were launched in 1961, and in both cases the Agena second-stage rocket failed. With Ranger I it failed to reignite, so the craft was left in its Parking Orbit, and atmospheric friction finally brought it down. In the case of Ranger II, the Agena lost its attitude stabilization and tumbled. Fortunately, it didn't reignite, and the whole mess decayed.

Rangers III, IV and V were scheduled closely behind I and II, and JPL had provided them with different payloads. They put a seismometer package aboard, intended to investigate quake activity after a soft landing on the moon. Al Hibbs says, "It was the most sensitive seismometer in the world, so sensitive that a truck passing on the street would knock it off scale. We'd expected that we'd get one to the moon before the Russians got a truck there." The instrument weighed 57 pounds and was encased in a balsa-wood sphere. The probe had a retromotor to reduce speed, and the balsa was to absorb the rest of the landing impact. There was also a TV camera, a radar experiment, and a gamma-radiation analyzer aboard.

Ranger III performed flawlessly until the terminal maneuver which was to reverse the probe for the lunar landing. It was programmed to perform a pitch maneuver first, in which it lifted its nose up and through 180° to turn end for end. Then it was to perform a yaw maneuver and slew around so that the retrorocket would be pointing directly down at the lunar surface.

(The expressions "pitch," "roll," and "yaw" can be understood by visualizing a sailboat. When the prow heaves up and down, that's pitch. When the mast heels over from side to side, that's roll. If the boat does not point in the direction in which it's going — yachtsmen say, "Look where she's going, and go where she's looking" — but skids its prow to the left or the right as it moves forward, that's yaw. Spacecraft are capable of blundering into all of them simultaneously, to the despair of everybody.)

Ranger III performed its pitch move, started its yaw move, and then suddenly repeated the pitch move and went into a pitch and yaw repetition, completely out of control. But Gordon Kautz of the Ranger Project Section at JPL says, "Even if this hadn't happened, the mission would have been degraded because Ranger III had been injected into an orbit which could not be corrected by the midcourse maneuver. The craft was bound to miss the moon. All that could result was a fly-by and some TV pictures.

"With Ranger IV, the central clock in the probe failed shortly after injection into orbit, and the craft lost some of its timing. Everything went haywire, and the craft was lost. Ranger V acquired the sun, but then the power subsystem failed, and it too is lost somewhere out there."

After five failures there were thorough investigations (the engineers call it Failure Mode Analysis) by JPL and NASA, and the Ranger program was again revised. The Manned Space Flight program had come into being, and NASA wanted a photographic mission instituted rapidly to help select a site for a landing on the moon. After Ranger V, the scientific experiments were scrubbed from Rangers VI to IX; all they were to carry was TV cameras. What was even more important, NASA dropped the sterilization constraint which had been imposed on Rangers III, IV, and V.

They had been heated to 125° C. for twenty-four hours, and there was also a terminal sterilization inside the shroud protecting the craft, using ethylene oxide, a deadly gas. Kautz says, "The heat was rough on the electronic parts, which may be why these Rangers failed. It was questionable as to why sterilization continued to be required because we couldn't see the need for it. There weren't any biological experiments planned for the moon."

The sterilization precaution is the answer to biologists' fears that planetary probes might carry terrestrial organisms to their targets, contaminating them, and ruining them as virgin ground for the investigations of alien life forms. This was why biologists were alarmed when the Russians crash-landed the Venus 3 probe on Venus in March, 1966; they had no way of knowing how thoroughly Venus 3 had been sterilized. Many people are under the impression that the hostile environment of deep space is automatically fatal to life. It is not.

George Hobby, a biologist with the JPL Space Sciences Division, says, "Cold will not destroy microorganisms; it preserves them. They may form spores. High vacuum has little or no effect on most spore forms. We've experimented with spores in vacuum chambers, and left them in for over a hundred days, and the vacuum did not destroy them. Ultraviolet radiation would kill every exposed organism on board a probe in a short time, but we have no guarantee that uv radiation would reach every corner and cranny in the craft. Some spores would certainly survive, and you may only need one to do the damage."

Consequently, contamination control is still required for planetary probes, and the agitation of biologists over the Venus 3 landing was not calmed by Russian assurances that the probe had been sterilized. They know how difficult it is to achieve safe sterilization. Don Burcham, project manager of the Mars Voyager mission, says, "There must be less than one chance in ten thousand of contaminating Mars."

Asked how the one in ten thousand contamination restraint compared with the sterilization requirements for a surgical operation, Burcham said, "They've run tests in a regular open operation in a hospital, and they get a contamination of six hundred bacteria per minute in the wound. The sterile requirements are far more severe for a Mars probe than for a surgical operation."

Voyager was planned as a soft-landing mission to Mars and was still in the conceptual phase. Its primary objective was to be the investigation of life and life environment on

Mars. The payload was to consist of a bus, carrying a capsule and equipped with a retroengine. The bus would approach Mars, go into orbit around Mars, and then drop the capsule to the surface. The bus itself would not land.

The study of alien life forms is called exobiology, and one of its main purposes is to discover the fundamental nature of life and its genesis. So far there have been three classic experiments on earth which have provided some of the answers. They were all postulated on the fact that the basic building blocks of life on earth are amino acids, nucleotides, and ATP. Amino acids are the essential components of protein. Nucleotides make up the famous nucleic acids, DNA and RNA, which are the key to the Genetic Code. ATP, adenosine triphosphate, stores and transfers energy in cells. Without these three you can't have life as we know it on earth.

Harold Urey and Stanley Miller at the University of Chicago theorized that the earth's proto-atmosphere contained methane gas and ammonia gas. Between them these gases contained the components of amino acids, but the question was, how might they have formed the acids? If that proto-atmosphere were turbulent it might have generated electrical storms which might have set off the reaction. In 1953, Urey and Miller passed electrical discharges through methane and ammonia, and produced amino acids.

John Oro of the University of Houston examined the organic diagram of cyanide and noticed that it seemed to be made up of many nucleotide molecules in various combinations. The question was whether cyanides, also probably present in the earth's proto-atmosphere, could be broken up to produce nucleotides. Oro reasoned that the earth was much hotter billions of years ago, so he subjected cyanide to long slow heat, and got his nucleotides. This was in 1960. Three years later, Cyri Ponnamperuma, now at NASA's Ames Research Center, demonstrated that ATP could be easily formed, too.

"The building blocks are not difficult to form, chemically," Dr. Gerald Soffen of the Jet Propulsion Laboratory says, "but the next step in the biogenic pathway is still difficult to understand, and may be considerably more difficult to perform. How do nucleotides form nucleic acid, which is capable of self-replication?"

The problem is analogous to the mystery of wine. What transforms simple grapes into a sophisticated wine? You start with grape sugar and end up with an elegant alcohol. What triggers the process? The answer is yeast. Its cells seed the grapes and act on them to cause fermentation. Is it possible that the earth was seeded with nucleic acids from space eons ago? Like yeast they may have brought about the transformation of the building blocks into complex organic life. It would only need a trace to start the nucleotides building up into nucleic acids on a tremendous scale in the primitive broth of the earth. This is why Dr. Soffen wonders whether terrestrial life was originated here or extraterrestrially.

"If one goes to Mars and finds life there of a separate origin from life on earth, then what? One says either Mars and earth have each been seeded from a separate origin, or each has generated a different form of life. But either means that life is probably not unique to earth. It suggests that the universe is teeming with life, and if this is so, who are we to say that we're the highest form? This gives us an added incentive for contacting other stars and other planets."

Asked how biologists could tell whether life on Mars had

a different origin, Dr. Soffen gave some fascinating Sherlock Holmes clues. "All biologically produced sugar on earth is dextro-rotatory; that is, when polarized light is passed through it, the light is rotated to the right. On the other hand, all biologically produced amino acids are levo-rotatory; they rotate polarized light to the left. The opposites of these substances are known, but are biologically inactive. This suggests that all life on earth had one single origin.

"If there is life on Mars, does it produce right-handed sugar and left-handed amino acids like the earth? That would suggest that it had the same origin as life on earth. But if Mars produces the reverse, left-handed sugar and right-handed amino acids, it would suggest that their life had a separate origin from terrestrial life. Also, the genetic code operates in the same way for all terrestrial animals. If we find a code operating differently on Mars, that too would indicate that life there is of separate origin."

The JPL biologists were studying the potential of a number of experiments for the Voyager mission, all intended to detect microorganisms on Mars, if any. Two of the most interesting are "Gulliver" and "Wolf Trap." In Operation Gulliver, a projectile is shot out of the experiment package, dragging a length of string after it; a sort of miniature whaler's harpoon. After the string has lain on the Martian soil for a time, it is automatically wound back onto a spool inside the package. There is a vial of culture medium within the spool, and this is cracked open automatically, saturating the string.

If any microorganisms have been brought back, adhering to the string, it's hoped they will grow. The experimenters will know whether they're there and growing by using a rather clever device which they call a "tag substrate." Say the culture medium contains glucose, which is a sugar and whose molecule consists of carbon, hydrogen, and oxygen. Most organisms feed on glucose and burn it to carbon dioxide and water. Now suppose that instead of making glucose with ordinary carbon, you make it with radioactive carbon, called carbon-14. Atoms of carbon-14 will remain radioactive no matter how they are combined with other atoms, or no matter what ordinary chemical transformation they are involved in.

If the organisms captured by Gulliver thrive on the glucose in the culture medium, they may eliminate carbon dioxide, and the carbon atoms in the carbon dioxide will be radioactive. There is a Geiger tube above the culture chamber which can detect this radioactivity. Signals from the Geiger tube will be transmitted to earth by radio, and will tell whether the organisms have released the radioactive carbon. Changes in the counting rate of the detector will indicate whether or not the organism is reproducing and multiplying.

But George Hobby says, "We have no way of knowing whether Martian organisms can live on our pre-prepared culture medium, or whether they'll produce tagged carbon dioxide, or whether some non-biological property of Martian soil will produce radioactive carbon. Also, is dumping the organisms into a liquid medium the right thing? Mars may not have a liquid phase for bacteria. Nobody knows. The Gulliver experiment is one way of finding out the answers to these questions."

In Operation Wolf Trap, dust is sucked into a chamber, and filtered to block out the large particles. The microparticles are deposited in a glass culture flask containing growth medium and investigated with a light-scattering technique. A beam of light shines into one side of the flask. If any of the dust particles prove to be microorganisms and if they multiply in the culture medium, they will cloud the medium and increase the scattered light reaching a photomultiplier on the opposite side of the flask. This change in light signal is reported back by radio.

Hobby says, "The biological experiments will attempt to answer the one most important question: Is there life there? But if we can only do a few experiments on each mission, how can we detect life (if it is there) with the fewest number of experiments and missions? The fact that Martian life may be very different than earth life makes it difficult to decide. Two opposite points of view are possible.

"One suggests that these experiments be postponed until we can answer some environmental questions: Does strong solar ultraviolet radiation reach the surface? What is the atmosphere like? What are the constituents of the soil? What is the temperature on and beneath the surface? Answers to some of these questions will make it possible to design better life detection experiments. The other says: Since the question of life on the planet is so important, take a chance on the long shot and try to detect life before we contaminate the planet."

Before moving on to other NASA scientific missions, there's one further question about life on other worlds that should be answered. People often ask, "All right, let's say there are other life forms somewhere in the universe, and let's say they're more advanced than we are. Then why haven't we heard from them?" Dr. Robert Jastrow of the Institute for Space Studies in New York has a provocative

The OSO satellite being fitted into the nose cone of the three-stage Delta rocket. The satellite is compacted for the launch.

ssembling the OSO satellite at the Ball Brothers Research Corporation. ne of the basketball covers protecting the titanium gas bottles can be seen.

OSO, the Orbiting Solar Observatory, the subject of this biography. All the members of the OSO family look substantially alike.

Special effects photograph of the OSO satellite to simulate its appearance in space. The blurred gas bottles on their outrigger arms indicate that the "wheel" is spinning, while the "sail" remains pointed at the sun.

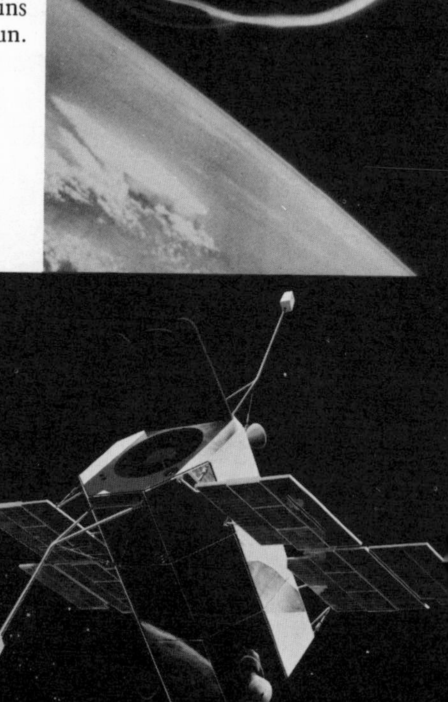

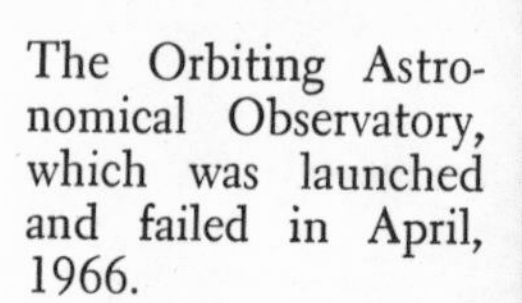

The Orbiting Astronomical Observatory, which was launched and failed in April, 1966.

The OSO satellite and its Delta rocket vehicle being readied for the launch at Cape Kennedy.

R. H. Gablehouse, the BBRC project manager.

Laurence Hogarth, the colonial administrator, project manager for the OSO program. He understood the meaning of "accountability."

William Pickering, director of the Jet Propulsion Laboratory, another strong-minded NASA independent.

John Lindsay, the loner, who inspired and maneuvered the OSO program into being. He never let his right hand know what his left hand was doing.

Harry Goett, the maverick director of the Goddard Space Flight Center, who backed his fellow maverick Lindsay and the OSO program.

reply. Jastrow says, "It's a valid question. After all, the American Indians didn't find Western Europe; it was the other way around.

"But look at it this way. Say they've sent out probes to other stars. Such a probe is circling our sun, waiting for a sign that one of our planets has intelligent life advanced enough to communicate with. What would be such a sign? It couldn't be visual. Obviously it would have to be radio noise. Now we've only been making radio noise for the past sixty years, so say the alarm system of the probe was tripped sixty years ago.

"But statistical analysis tells us that the stars average four hundred light years distant from each other, so that alarm will probably take at least four hundred years to reach home. Then their response and attempt to contact us will take another four hundred years to reach us. We can't expect to hear from another star for at least seven centuries. Whether our civilization will still be here to listen is another question."

Voyager was still in the planning stage, but Mariner had a full head of steam. Mariners I and II, the Venus missions, had already been launched. Mariner I was boosted up in July, 1962, went off course, and was destroyed by the Range Safety Officer within sight of the Cape. Mariner II was launched one month later and encountered Venus in a fly-by 109 days later. Among other things, its telemetry reported that Venus had no magnetic field and had a high surface temperature, close to 800° F.

The Mars missions, Mariners III and IV, were being readied. They were to carry eight experiments investigating cosmic rays, cosmic dust, magnetic fields, ultraviolet radiation, and the solar wind. The most dramatic experiment, of course, was the photography of Mars by television camera, and this is worthy of a fuller description.

With the best earth-based telescopes we can see detail on Mars equivalent to the detail we see on the moon with the naked eye. The TV scan hoped to magnify this fifty times. It would cover a strip stretching from pole to pole, taking twenty-two photographs of areas approximately two hundred by two hundred kilometers, and revealing objects three kilometers in size. (One kilometer equals .621 miles.) The pictures were to be taken at an altitude of 5500 miles. It was possible to have the probe pass Mars much closer, but if it did it would be moving so fast that the pictures would be blurred.

The transmission of the pictures back to earth was by telemetry code. The TV equipment was a single tube with a photosensitive plate divided into a matrix of forty thousand dots, or picture elements, measuring two hundred by two hundred dots. A scanner inspects each dot in turn, estimates its brightness, and gives it a value from zero to sixty-three. Then the brightness number and position of the dot are transmitted back to earth. On earth, the process is reversed, and a reproduction of the picture is built up, dot by dot.

The Canopus sensor was ingenious, too. The problem was how to make sure that the Mariner probe would have its camera pointed directly at Mars when it passed in the encounter. The theoreticians at JPL worked it out that if a sensor on the probe could find Canopus, a bright star in the constellation Carina, and lock on it, the probe would be maintained in exactly the right attitude for the encounter.

The Canopus sensor used the principles of the Ball

Brothers rocket-pointing device, but was a much more sophisticated system. It could register and transmit light intensities, and was provided with gates to eliminate objects that were too bright or too dim. Dan Schneiderman, the Mariner project manager, explained, "The sensor kept locking on stars within these limits. We kept getting intensity readings back, and as soon as we got a reading on a star, we instructed the probe to drop that one and search again."

The instructions, of course, were by radio command. The craft obeyed them by altering its roll angle with gas jets, so that its sensor could have a look at another sector of space. Schneiderman said, "We were able to draw up a plot of what stars the craft was looking at, compare this with a chart drawn up in advance of the location and probable intensities of the stars, and then pop it over to Canopus."

I've already told you about the sensor's bewilderment by dust in space, and the stern lecture that Schneiderman was forced to read it. The Mariner's marvelous closeups of Mars were released shortly after the encounter in July, 1965. The Russian papers studiously ignored the triumph. It must have hurt them almost as much as Sputnik hurt us.

At Goddard they were going ahead with the weather satellites. The second generation Nimbus family was in preparation. The Tiros series was in orbit, taking hundreds of pictures a day, covering about twenty-five per cent of the earth's surface. W. G. Stroud, formerly chief of Aeronomy and Meteorology, now chief of Advanced Planning, said, "The significant coverage is daily. Our short-term forecasts, ranging from eighteen to thirty-six hours, are pretty good, but this is more or less due to the persistence of weather. You'd be right seventy-five per cent of the time if you predicted that tomorrow's weather will be like today's.

"The long-range forecast, from thirty to sixty days, is the science of climatology, and it's not too precise. The best you can do is predict that it'll be hotter or cooler, or there'll be more rain or less rain.

"Where forecasting is poor is in the middle range, the seven-day forecast. This is an extremely important area. Everybody wants to plan a week ahead; entertainment, fairs, sports, picnics, airlines, weekend trips, and so on. But we don't have forecasts for this period. The middle range is a characteristic of planetary wave phenomena. These waves are the fronts, the flow of energy from the equatorial regions to the polar regions. They have a period of about seven days, up to the poles and back. The clouds organize themselves to reflect this distribution of pressure and wind field."

The weather satellites send back cloud pictures, radiometric maps of reflected sunlight, and thermal maps in the infrared showing the thermal balance of the energy radiated out from the earth's surface. (These maps are beautiful enough to be framed and hung on a wall as works of art.) The advantage of the weather satellites is that they provide global measurements; up to their advent no one had ever realized the vast scale of the weather. Their disadvantage is the fact that no one has yet been able to devise a technique for them to measure temperature, barometric pressure, or winds. These are essential for weather prediction.

Goddard is attempting to develop a new system for these measurements. They've given the project the regrettable acronym of GIRLS, for Global Interrogation, Recording, and Looking System, and the clumsy hand of whoever contrived that title ought to be smacked. Goddard is establishing a network of ground-based automatic stations which will broadcast information about temperature, pressure, and winds to a satellite, which will collect the data and transmit it to a center.

Mr. Stroud loves weather. He says, "We're living in a sea of air that sustains and harasses us. Without an atmosphere there would be no blue sky, no clouds, no sunsets. Without rain we'd be living in an atmosphere of dust; rain keeps the atmosphere clean. Without weather we'd live like goldfish in a constant environment."

Mr. Stroud is angry about the weather. He says, "I don't pretend to understand the rationale of natural attitudes toward the weather. Less than one twentieth of the earth's atmosphere is under observation today. The weather bureau has no funds. Congress is unsympathetic, and there's no public sympathy either. The weather bureau is kicked around like a stepchild. Our hope is that the weather satellites can provide a cheap way of doing something about this. It's not today, but we're working toward it."

The Theory and Analysis department at Goddard was very proud. Reduction of the tracking data on Vanguard revealed that the satellite was reeling in its orbit like a drunken sailor, and led to some interesting deductions. The earth is not shaped like a flattened orange, but more like a pear, with the massive end on top. The atmosphere is not evenly distributed around the earth, but bulges at the equator as a result of the earth's rotation. Sunspots affect solar radiation which, in turn, exerted a gentle pressure on Vanguard. Waxing and waning sunspots led to changes in the radiation pressure on the satellite, which contributed to its drunken career.

NASA and the Department of Defense had decided to

build Syncom, the communications satellite, as a joint program. DOD would supply the ground communications, and NASA would provide the spacecraft, telemetry, and the command system. They had started building three Syncoms and were bogged down in a morass of struggle with contractors, inadequate materials, and inability to obtain high priority parts. They were forced to postpone the launch of Syncom I for a year.

They had had an unsettling experience with the flight test of Echo I from Wallops Island in Virginia. The Public Information Office thought that perhaps the press ought to be warned of the test, and asked the scientists if the communications satellite could be seen. The scientists said no, not unless you knew exactly where to look for Echo. So there wasn't any pre-flight announcement.

Echo was launched, and burst into flame a few miles up. The satellite was sheathed in aluminum to provide the radio reflector, and the sheathing stripped off and burned, producing a dazzling spectral effect. The entire seaboard around Virginia was in a tizzy. People were jamming the phone lines with reports of Unidentified Flying Objects, and even airline pilots were calling their flight towers wanting to know what the hell was going on. This was the last time that the PIO permitted a launch without a pre-flight announcement.

The Sounding Rocket program was accelerating, with nearly a hundred launches a year from Wallops Island, Fort Churchill in Manitoba, and White Sands in New Mexico. There was a large stable of rockets, costing anywhere from six thousand dollars to one hundred and fifty thousand dollars each, and giving experimenters anywhere from five to thirty minutes above the atmosphere. There was still a contest between sounding rockets and spacecraft. The rockets were much cheaper, much quicker to launch, and each experiment could be self-contained; that is, no one had to share space with anyone else.

Some of the rocket research programs were rather odd. There were grenade experiments in which grenades were exploded in sequence at various altitudes, to estimate atmospheric pressure, density, and winds by their sound waves; micrometeorite collections in buckets of grease; joyrides for protozoa to see if free fall affected them; and preliminary tests in preparation for satellite missions.

Many of these tests were for the future Orbiting Astronomical Observatory, and Eleanor Pressly, head of the Rocket Vehicles Section, says, "In the rivalry between the sounding rockets and the OAO, the rockets seem to be fighting back. Certainly whenever the astronomy crowd comes down to White Sands for a sounding shot, the rocket crowd shakes in its shoes. Something always seems to go wrong. The wildest was the incident of the electric blanket.

"They use electric blankets to keep the rockets warm. No, I'm serious. If the propellants get too cold you don't get full efficiency. So when the rocket's on the pad they plug in plain ordinary electric blankets and keep it wrapped up until launch. Well, this time one of the blankets caught fire, and everybody ran for their lives; the astronomers faster than anyone else."

One of the escapees was Dr. Jim Kupperian, who was slowly nursing OAO along. OAO was going to be a giant; thirteen feet long, weighing thirty-five hundred pounds and flying a beryllium telescope mirror three feet in diameter, and ten other telescopes in combination. It was a double-ended observatory operating two prime experiments; ultraviolet broad band photometry, using seven telescopes, and gamma-ray and X-ray measurements, using four telescopes.

"The astronomical program is the extension of the spectrum," Kupperian says. "At present we're working in the ultraviolet; on the ground we see only the red tail of the spectrum. We're after data on the hot young stars that are only ten thousand to a hundred thousand years old. This is the study of star formation and evolution, and it's almost essential if we're going to be able to say anything about cosmology. The little data we've gotten already from rockets has already changed our theories.

"X rays don't reach the earth any more than uv. The question that OAO will help answer is, what is the source of X radiation? On the ground we've picked up a half dozen sources of X rays from near the galactic center; the Crab nebula, Scorpius, and others. Right now we're getting more X rays from Scorpius than from the sun. These will be some of OAO's objectives.

"There's a lot of wild speculation on what may be discovered. One is the 'Neutron Star.' It's a star composed of squeezed-together neutrons, so hot that all the radiation comes out as X rays. It's not much bigger than the earth, but weighs more than the sun. It's been speculated that Neutron Stars may be the source of X rays. The trouble with the theory is, we've discovered too many X-ray sources, and there can't be that many Neutron Stars. The reason is, Neutron Stars are supposed to have a life of only fifty years. The universe can't be running down that fast.

"The gamma-ray telescopes will do a general survey of gamma rays in the galaxy. Gamma rays are produced by the collision of cosmic rays with hydrogen gas. If you know the gas distribution in the galaxy, and check the gamma-ray distribution, you can work backwards and guess about cosmic ray distribution. This is an exploration of galactic structure.

"What we're going to do is fly X-ray telescopes, gamma-ray telescopes, and other instruments to change the contrast of the universe. We're going to look at it in a different wavelength and compare it with visible observations. It's the *differences* between them that we're looking for.

"Our problem is time in orbit. That telescope's going to be up there and it's got to be used all the time. You don't get a night off because of rainy weather and have a chance to figure out what to do next. We have to prepare in advance. OAO's central clock has a 62½-second 'minute.' I don't know why. But at the end of every minute the craft has to do something. It has to have a programmed memory, but you can't prepare for everything in advance. Talk about tough decisions! We're really putting all our eggs in one basket."

Like many other NASA scientists, Kupperian is deeply concerned about the huge amounts of money being spent. He said, "The OAO will cost hundreds of millions. The question most often asked is, 'After that big an outlay, what will you discover?' " He shook his head. "You can't answer that. *That's* discovery."

Kupperian's Orbiting Astronomical Observatory, along with Lindsay's Advanced Orbiting Solar Observatory, marked the advent of what was called the Second Generation satellites in NASA's planning. They were enormous, highly sophisticated craft with a capacity for many complex functions. They were Cadillacs, compared to the early Model T satellites, and the fact that NASA was able to plan them demonstrated that the space program was in high gear.

But that fact also meant that thunderclouds were gathering. A conflict was shaping up; a conflict which is inherent in the life cycle of any successful enterprise. When anything new is begun, it's the pioneer types who are asked to lead the way into the unknown. These are the independents with the courage to stand on their own two feet, experiment and improvise, and take full responsibility for the results. Harry Goett of Goddard, and William Pickering of the Jet Propulsion Laboratory belonged to this breed, and it was their understanding with NASA that they were to be given a free hand.

But once the pioneers have broken the trail and gotten the enterprise off to a successful start, management begins to move in on the operation; the lawyers, the accountants, the organization specialists. These are the "Headquarters Types" and their argument is, "The pioneering days are over. There's no longer any need for a free hand. Now you have a successful business going, and you must have management or you'll have chaos." They are opposed to maverick leadership; they want everything wrapped up in neat procedural packages.

JPL had been an independent research laboratory before it joined NASA, and Pickering still clung to this independence. JPL was coming into open conflict with the headquarters types in Washington, and was accused of deliberately provoking the battle. Harry Goett had succeeded magnificently in getting Goddard on its feet, and was not at all inclined to make any concessions to management philosophy. He, too, was coming into open conflict with the headquarters types, and was accused of being pathological in his defiance.

Unfortunately for JPL and Goddard, the headquarters types were closer to Congress, geographically and philosophically, than Pickering and Goett. They had the heavier guns, and they were bringing them to bear.

14

Death of a Satellite

"OSO was one long cliff-hanger," Hogarth said. It certainly was taking on some aspects of a Pearl White serial, and Hogarth was turning himself into the heavy. There had been his insistence on organization, method, and scheduling. Then his perting of Harvard had enraged Lindsay and the scientific community. Now he made a move that embroiled him with the General Accounting Office, the government's watchdog on public spending.

A tone command system for OSO-B had already been bought and paid for. After the freak disaster to OSO-I, Hogarth junked it and ordered a new digital command system. "This is the difference between piston engines and jets. Anyway, the decision was made for us. The Data and Tracking people convinced Goddard that we must never fly another tone command system." The trouble was, the decision cost $240,000.

Data retrieval and instrument operation aboard OSO-I had been controlled by simple tone commands, and apparently everybody except the accountants knew what had happened to that system over North Africa. Also, the Harvard experiment, which was the prime experiment on OSO-B, could not be performed satisfactorily with primitive tone commands. It required a more sophisticated system which would enable it to select any single wavelength in the ultraviolet for its examination of the sun. This was only possible with a digital command system, which is now used in all spacecraft.

In this system, commands are punched in paper tape as slots or holes. The tape is tested in a ground command verifier which has an array of white and red lights. If the command has been correctly punched, only the white lights will show. The command consists of two groups of digits. The first group is the address to which the command will be relayed. The second group is the command itself.

The command tape is run into a command encoder which issues the command, via radio, to the craft. There are two command decoders aboard OSO; one in the sail, handling traffic for the sail functions, and one in the wheel, handling all operations there. (There's also a spare decoder in the wheel, just in case anything goes wrong.) The command is addressed by number to whichever decoder is supposed to receive it. The decoder then selects the particular relay which is to receive the command itself, and passes it along.

The commands are carefully planned, punched and verified well in advance. The tracking stations broadcast them to the satellite as it makes its pass overhead. A good pass, one close to the zenith, will give a station some twelve minutes in which to maintain radio contact, but since a large portion of that time is taken up by the satellite's dumping of the data it collected on its last orbit, only about ten commands can be issued.

Sometimes all ten commands may be required to get just one thing done. Suppose you want a single wheel experiment turned off. First you command all the wheel experiments off. Then you issue commands, one by one, turning each wheel experiment on again, with the exception of the one you want off. Occasionally you can miss getting a command through when the satellite is momentarily blind to broadcasts from the ground because its antenna is not properly lined up on the earth.

There are four subsystems in a satellite; electric power, satellite control, telemetry and communications, and command. In OSO-B there was a capacity for one hundred forty commands spread through a marvelously intricate network, all covering for each other in an attempt to copper all bets. If, for instance, the spectograph unaccountably ignored its command to turn on, this might be overcome if the electric power subsystem had been programmed with a command which would feed power into all experiments to activate them. This is just another example of the careful pre-planning and anticipation of all possible failures which John New mentioned.

Urged on by the accountants, Congress was taking a closer look at the NASA program, and criticizing Hogarth's and almost everybody else's decisions by hindsight. One of the Goddard officials says, "It was bad enough when the White House was sending any visiting dignitary they didn't know what to do with down to us for a sight-seeing tour, but now congressmen were coming down and arguing with engineers about electronics." They were also holding hearings and asking profound questions like why was the Nimbus weather satellite taking longer to build and costing more than was originally estimated. Nimbus was another of the second generation satellites, and its construction was breaking new trails. Harry Goett snapped back, "Because no one has ever built a Nimbus before."

These were the opening guns in headquarters' attack on the mavericks, and although Goett was countering energetically, he had a premonition of defeat. He told me, "My job is a constant fight against cost accountants, and it's a losing struggle. When an operation is small, you can trust men, but when it gets big you can't manage by the seat of your pants, and then the accountants take over. You have to go into formal procedure, and procedure destroys creativity. Our problem is to maintain the flexibility of a small project in a big one. Ours is a team operation, but we have to make sure that teamwork doesn't squeeze the spark out of a man.

"There's been a trend to think that you don't have to know anything about a field to manage it; all you have to be is a good manager. It's also believed that all you have to do to make something successfully is to plan carefully. But you can't plan and foresee everything when you're building something absolutely new. It may work for building cars, but it will not work in the Research and Development field."

Speaking of the accountants' crackdown on OSO, Ranger, and other projects, Goett said, "The advantage that a sales department has over Research and Development in corporations is that when Sales asks for more money to try something, they can promise an immediate return which will show in the profit column; but when Research and Development asks for more money, all they can say is, 'Have faith.' That's our problem with the accountants."

By spring of 1963 the OSO-B experiment prototypes were delivered to BBRC at Boulder, not without many angry quarrels. The craft prototype went into tests in May. Hogarth says, "Ball Brothers were sore about having been pushed, but they wouldn't have been ready without it. The prototype was tested for two months, and had the usual teething problems."

The flight experiments were delivered in the fall of that year, but the flight model of the satellite was having difficulties; imperfect alloy castings, cracking deck plates, late deliveries, and substandard components. These were not cases of fraud, but of cowardice. Very often subcontractors can't obtain premium products in time to meet their schedules. They're afraid to wave the red flag and stop everything, as they should; instead they try to get by with second-choice materials.

This gave Hogarth an idea which promptly got him into hot water again. He suggested that NASA fly the OSO-B prototype first, take time to modify the flight model, and fly that next. His reasoning was that NASA would get two missions for the price of one. He was immediately howled down by the Goddard Reliability Assurance Committee which claimed that he was trying to cover up schedule trouble.

The committee also denounced the idea of flying a prototype. This is a ticklish question which has not yet been resolved. One school says that the extra stress of prototype testing fatigues the craft too much for use in space. The other school says not. Hogarth belonged to the latter, but was forced to shut up. The prototype was put aside, the badgering accelerated, the flight model of OSO-B was finally readied in April, 1964, and shipped to Cape Kennedy.

Two BBRC technicians went down for the launch; Sidney Dagle, a bright, eager kid who enjoyed the Boy Friday role which made him invaluable for a launch team, and Lott Gabel, an old-style craftsman in his fifties, who was the only man permitted to take apart and put together the craft. Lott and his wife drove down to Florida for the launch, turning the mission into a holiday. Hogarth flew down for the launch and was joined by Gabe Gablehouse, the BBRC program manager. Gablehouse is a short, thickset man who resembles Spencer Tracy. He is blunt and taciturn, the stereotype of the engineer.

The OSO-B was delivered to the Douglas hangar in the Area 39 bay quite early in the morning. Hogarth and Gablehouse met to drive over and supervise the alignment and spin-balance operations, but they were delayed, Hogarth says, "Some son of a bitch at Goddard was trying to pull off a dirty trick, and I was on the phone from the Cape to Goddard, boiling mad.

"After I hung up on Goddard I was still so mad that I remembered something Gabe had done that I was meaning to eat him out about, so we got into a fight which lasted for half an hour. Then Gabe went out to get a car for us, but I was still furious, so I called Goddard again and continued my scrap with them. Just as I was saying, 'Look, I've got to hang up now and go over to the spin-balance test,' Gabe rushed in, his face white. He said, 'It's blown up.' "

Hogarth and Gablehouse tore over to Area 39 to find out what had happened. The satellite had arrived at the Douglas hangar at five in the morning. Eight Douglas technicians were present, along with Sidney Dagle, Lott Gabel, and John Fassett, the NASA coordinator at the Cape. The payload was removed from the transporter by overhead crane, was immediately placed on a large beam scale, and the entire assembly, including the payload handling can, was weighed.

After the weigh-in the assembly was placed on the floor and the top half of the can was removed, exposing the payload, covered with a polyethylene bag which was to remain around the payload until the launch. However, it could be rolled up to give access to the satellite as required.

The payload was lifted out of the can, cleaned, and hoisted on top of the third-stage X-248 motor. The rocket motor was fueled, of course, because the distribution of its solid fuel weight had to be balanced along with the craft in the spin-balance test. By six in the morning, payload and motor were mated, clamped in place, and bolted. Then the polyethylene bag was rolled up and taped back, and the third stage and payload were aligned on a true vertical axis.

When the alignment was finished, a tube was attached for the purge of the payload with nitrogen gas to remove dust. Lott Gabel made some final mechanical adjustments. The Douglas men had finished their job and started to leave the hangar. Lott finished his tinkering and pulled the plastic cover down into place. He stepped back, took a look, didn't like the way the cover was hanging, stepped forward and adjusted it. The third-stage motor fired. Everything roared up in a mass of smoke and flame and smashed into a girder thirty feet overhead.

The payload was wrenched off by the impact and fell straight down. The motor zoomed off to the right at 3 G's and crashed into the hangar floor, just inside a door through which B. J. Billings, a Douglas technician, had passed a moment before. Four of the Douglas men were blown halfway across the hangar and badly burned. Three others were nearly crushed when an entire side of the hangar collapsed. Sidney Dagle, Lott Gabel, and John Fassett were killed.

The calamity plunged NASA into deep gloom, and to this day they're extremely reluctant to talk about it. Three fine men were dead. The satellite was ruined. "Now," Hogarth said grimly, "they were beginning to understand the meaning of accountability."

The premature ignition had been caused by a spark of static electricity, the same static electricity that makes your hair crackle under a comb in cold, dry weather. Gablehouse made an intensive study of the disaster with a research team from Cornell University. They reproduced the Douglas hangar conditions and experimented with X-248 motors, attempting to fire them with static electricity variously induced. They discovered that the motors could be ignited through a weird circuitry that was inherent in the motor structure, and that it was a miracle that this sort of accident had not happened before.

"As a matter of fact it had happened before," Gablehouse reported. "It was at a proving ground in Tulsa in November, 1963, but the information hadn't been released yet. If it had we'd have known and taken precautions."

Rocket motor manufacture has been revised to prevent any such accidents again.

Now Hogarth's organization paid off. He immediately ordered Ball Brothers to rebuild the OSO-B prototype for a launch, and gave it the working title of OSO-B2. BBRC said they could do the reconstruction by May, 1965. Hogarth demanded delivery by December, 1964. Despite the fact that many of the original experiments had survived the blowup, Hogarth decided to fly the flight spares, although he believes that he could have flown some of the originals.

"Lord knows, we needed everything we had. We cannibalized the wreckage. We were scraping the bottom of the barrel on some items. We took everything apart and went over it with a fine-tooth comb. Much electronic material has a limited shelf life. We had to fly a lot of iffy material, but I thought the prototype had a good enough chance of success to proceed."

Asked why he was so determined to fly the iffy prototype, Hogarth said, "We had to launch something; we had to keep the program going. We couldn't let down the experimenters who had been working on their experiments for years. This was the governing consideration. They all merited an immediate flight, and nothing else was available to fly their experiments."

He had learned to sympathize with Lindsay's rage for recognition, and all his feelings were for the experimenters. "They'd lost three or four years of their productive life, and that's a very big chunk. After all, we're doing science; there's no dignity in just putting a ball into the sky. We *had* to help the scientists get something on paper."

Asked if the Reliability Assurance Committee objected to flying the prototype, Hogarth smiled grimly. "There were no objections. They weren't asked."

In addition to the salvage of OSO-B2, Hogarth and Lindsay were also working on the construction of OSO-C, the third in the series, and organizing the following three satellites which were to have participating experiments from

England, France, and Italy. Both men were in a state of constant physical exhaustion.

Hogarth was being forced to play the tyrant in order to obtain excellence, and at the same time was forced to display a coolness and confidence which he really did not feel. The amber worry bead made its appearance more and more often. At last the energy drain culminated in a return of a boyhood ailment, a syncopation of the heart, which had all the effects of a heart attack. It was accompanied by an intermittent fever. Hogarth was badly frightened. He had difficulty sleeping. The fever impaired his vision. His usually healthy features become blanched and haggard. He took to using the elevator instead of running up the one flight to his office, and he was ashamed of his weakness.

Lindsay was driving harder and harder in his race with time. He was terrified of growing old. He talked about how harsh nature was, and he kept quizzing Hogarth about how it felt to grow old. It was a horrible thing to him. He would talk about women losing their looks and having their insides out. He felt that he was approaching fifty and getting nowhere. He felt that he was in a vacuum. Hogarth found it impossible to reassure his friend.

Despite the illness and the strain, the team got the job done, OSO-B2 was in the can ready for delivery to Cape Kennedy in December, 1964. Hogarth wanted a launch well before Christmas. "Nobody does good work during Christmas." But there were many other launches stacked up and waiting. The Cape put B2 down to January, which was just as well. When the craft was delivered to the Cape it had so many bugs that it took them a month to prepare it for flight.

They took B2 apart and spread it out on the hangar floor.

There were miles of wire connections and circuits to check. Fatigued capacitors, resistors, and transistors had to be juiced up and peaked. The satellite's radio transmitter was subject to fits of hysteria and emitted loud shrieks, or "birdies." The danger of a birdie is that it might be picked up by the satellite's radio receiver at the moment when a command was being transmitted to it. The birdie could alter one bit in the command, with fatal results.

The satellite's transmitter only produced birdies when its antenna was down in the launch position. (Everything is compacted tightly within a shroud for the launch.) Hogarth decided to launch B2 with its radio transmitter off. It could be activated later when B2 was safely in space. This immediately triggered a hot controversy. It meant that they would be launching a mute satellite, and wouldn't know where it was after it took off. Hogarth insisted that they could trust the Johannesburg tracking station to get a fix on the bird's first pass, and let them know immediately. There were excellent communications between Joburg, Goddard, and the Cape. B2 wouldn't be lost. He won the argument.

By the end of January, 1965, B2 was reassembled and given its terminal tests. Just before it was moved to the launch pad, John Fassett's widow came to the Cape to see it. The mission team was deeply moved by this generous and courageous gesture, and escorted Mrs. Fassett through the hangar with the gallantry of royal equerries.

OSO-B2 was boosted up in February, 1965. Again it was a noon launch so that the craft could be phased into an orbit with a plane parallel to the solar vector. Watching the launch on the control center television screen was agonizing, as it always is. As the rocket vehicle flamed upward it approached the top of the TV screen, but the TV tube is curved, and the optical distortion made it look as though the rocket had broken and was toppling over. There were gasps from the novices.

The team waited tensely for the orbit fix from Johannesburg. Five minutes after the launch, the Joburg tracking station went dead. "Cliff-hanger," Hogarth muttered. They waited ninety-six minutes while the mute satellite made its first orbit. They had no way of knowing whether or not the craft had opened up from its fetal position within the shroud and gone into its operational mode. That was the horror.

Then it was time for it to make its first pass over the Fort Myers tracking station in Florida. There was an open line to Fort Myers, and everybody waited for the word, hating each other. Fort Myers nicked the bird as it came over the radar fence, and got a fix. The craft was commanded to start its radio transmitter. The team watched the dials and the green face of the oscilloscope on the radio reception panel.

The dial needles began to quiver slightly. The level line of light across the oscilloscope turned into a sinuous curve. Gablehouse switched on the loudspeaker which began a rhythmic warble, rather like a peanut whistle. That was the satellite broadcasting its housekeeping information. It was alive. It was no longer OSO-B2; it had become OSO-II.

Hogarth remained casual, although he seemed to swell slightly. Later he confided that it had been a tremendous experience. The Explorers and the first OSO had been somebody else's property, and Hogarth says, "I don't want someone else's wife. I guess you don't get much fun out of life if you don't want someone else's wife, but I don't want her. I don't want someone else's dog, either."

But OSO-II was his first very own bird, and a part of him was in space. There's such an emotional involvement with a man's first satellite that he's never the same. A man's first satellite is like his first love affair.

15

The Missions Accelerate

Now let's return to that experimenters' conference at the Goddard Space Flight Center with which we began Chapter Two. It'll be interesting to see how much of the space jargon we can understand now. But before we do, let's put the meeting into perspective with a look at the other accelerating NASA programs in progress at the same time, March, 1965, and their subsequent development.

Dr. Bill Hess's office is opposite the OSO conference room, and Hess is always happy to talk about the work of the Theoretical Division which he heads. "What are we working on now? Well, we have a group doing quantum mechanics to study atomic phenomena. Nuclear physics can't give us all the answers, or at least we don't know the right questions to ask. The field of atomic physics may be able to answer some of them.

"We've got people studying the atmosphere of stars. Satellites have given us some big surprises, especially in the ultraviolet examination of hot stars. We're studying the ionosphere for the production of atmospheric particles produced by sunlight and collisions. You don't find these in the sea-level atmosphere.

"We have a group studying radiation belts. How are they formed? How are they distorted by the solar wind? The radiation belt discovery created a tremendous stir because it was totally unanticipated, and in a major way changed our understanding of our environment. It's intensely dramatic to find out that we'll be fried alive if we go a thousand miles into space."

The theoreticians are also studying the effects of trapped particles on the aurora borealis. In the fall of 1966 Hess will try to create an artificial aurora by flying a small electron accelerator on an Aerobee rocket which will give him five minutes above one hundred kilometers. The accelerator will shoot a beam of electrons down into the atmosphere and, hopefully, produce a small aurora. The shot will be from Wallops Island on the coast of Virginia, and all airline pilots take notice.

Other interesting problems: Jupiter has a very large radio radiation belt, Saturn does not. Why the difference? Both rotate rapidly which should mean that they have similar magnetic fields and belts of trapped particles which emit the radio radiation. Are Saturn's rings doing something to block its radiation? On the other hand, the Mars encounter revealed that Mars has no magnetic field. But Mars rotates almost as rapidly as the earth and should have a similar magnetic field. Why not?

Tektites, those odd meteorites thought to have originated on the moon, were found to contain coesite, which is a deformed quartz that has been squeezed together by impact events. That means that tektites are the result of an impact process, but did the impact take place when they were blasted off the moon, or when they came crashing down to earth from somewhere else in space? There's a hot fight about it today.

The mystery of Mercury has at last been solved. For centuries astronomers believed that Mercury revolved around the sun exactly the way the moon revolves around the earth, always presenting the same face. The trouble with this was the fact that measurements of the dark side of the planet revealed that it was too hot for a hemisphere that never faced the sun. Where did the heat come from?

Now we know. Recent observations have revealed that Mercury rotates in a very odd way; once every fifty-six days in its eighty-eight-day revolution around the sun. The curious thing about it is that it's caused by the sun's tremendous attraction which trips the planet in its orbit and makes it turn over. In other words, Mercury literally flips.

The Orbiting Astronomical Observatory was being readied for launch in March, 1966. In addition to its many objectives, Jim Kupperian was hoping for a look at some quasars, which are quasi-stellar sources. Quasars are the most exciting astronomical discovery of the twentieth century.

Radio astronomers had been looking for radio sources in the universe for decades. A few years ago they found some fairly bright radio objects with no optical objects to go with them. They enlisted the aid of visual astronomers and started trying to correlate these radio sources with optical sources. They found some strange ones; dull optical objects with spectacular radio emissions, great distances away, and moving at half the speed of light. These are the quasars.

Several of the quasars are unique galaxies, putting out gigantic amounts of radio energy equivalent to the entire mass of one hundred millions suns. That is, if you annihilated one hundred million suns and converted their mass into radio energy, it would equal the radio energy from a single quasar. This is far more than the energy produced by nuclear processes, and consequently it's theorized that the radio emission is produced by the gravitational collapse of a galaxy, which transforms kinetic energy into radio energy.

But there's a paradox in this theory. Such a gravitational collapse should make quasars disappear from the universe altogether. It would produce a "gravitational well" so deep and so powerful that the quasar would pass beyond the event horizon. In other words, the gravitational attraction would become so strong that photons and all other electromagnetic emissions couldn't get out, with the result that no one would be able to see them. The quasar might very well turn out to be a gravitational hole in the universe.

Alas for Jim Kupperian's hopes, OAO was doomed, and it succumbed to the chronic ailment that plagues most spacecraft, power failure. As was said before, we desperately need a breakthrough in battery technology.

After five launch attempts had failed, OAO was finally boosted into orbit on April 8, 1966. Everyone was concentrating on the problem of whether it would find and lock on its target stars. OAO found the stars, locked on them, and then began to lose and regain the lock. The tension mounted during the subsequent orbits. A day later, OAO's central clock began running ten minutes late.

Neither of these was necessarily fatal to the mission, but then the primary battery system overheated, and the power began to drain. They sent a command to the satellite to switch to the redundant, or spare battery system. It refused to obey. The command was repeated and the craft finally obeyed, but then it changed its mind and stubbornly went back to the overheated primary system. Two days after the launch all power was gone and the satellite was dead.

A NASA Failure Review Board is currently investigating the tragedy (to the scientific world it is *the* tragedy of the decade) and reappraising the entire program for observatory class satellites. Jim Kupperian has three more OAO's waiting, and if the Failure Review Board gives him the go-ahead, he hopes to launch another Orbiting Astronomical Observatory in early 1967.

The Syncom team reports one mystery, one success, and one miracle. Syncom I was launched in February, 1963. It had a three-minute test tape aboard, prepared to check all communications facilities. The tape ended with "The Star Spangled Banner." Syncom I failed, suddenly and totally, five and a half hours after launch. They couldn't put their finger on what happened. There wasn't room for any extensive housekeeping instrumentation on board for information to be sent back.

So they fixed everything on Syncom II and added a little more instrumentation. The craft was launched in July, 1963, and behaved like a charm. It oscillates from 30° North to 30° South, and moves a half a degree or four hundred miles westward each day. Before its life ends they hope to move it around the world.

They decided to give Syncom III an equatorial orbit, and hoped to place it within five degrees of the equator. After NASA's little hassle with Nigeria over the tracking ship, the satellite was launched in August, 1964, with fantastic success. Syncom III is a jewel, hanging over the middle of the Pacific Ocean at an altitude of 22,300 miles, virtually motionless. Actually, of course, its orbital speed almost exactly matches the earth's speed of revolution, which is three-tenths of a mile per second at the equator.

Syncom's orbit has a quarter-degree inclination to the equator, and oscillates a bare two hundred miles to the north and south each day. Its velocity is just a shade slower than the earth's, so it's drifting west at the rate of one-one hundredth of a degree, or eight miles a day. It's so steady that ground stations can put their radar on it and go home. It doesn't demand any tracking.

Syncom III is the communications satellite that transmitted the TV broadcast of the Tokyo Olympics in 1964. They had an interesting problem with the broadcast. The pictures were relayed by Syncom; the sound track was transmitted by cable. This meant that whereas the pictures were traveling fifty thousand miles, from Tokyo up to the satellite and then down to the States, the sound was only traveling six thousand miles under the Pacific via cable. Sound and sight arrived at different times and had to be held up and resynchronized before being broadcast to the TV public.

William Stroud was still struggling with the problem of teaching weather satellites to record temperature, air pressure, and winds. He was now working on an alternative plan for GIRLS. The idea was a network of thousands of weather balloons flying at altitudes from fifteen to twenty thousand feet. The trouble was, they'd be in the airlanes and would form a navigation hazard. Stroud was trying to develop a balloon that wouldn't destroy a plane if they collided.

John Lindsay, in addition to struggling with the problems of the Advanced Orbiting Solar Observatory and preparing his experiments for OSO-C and the subsequent members of the family, had come up with a daring concept. It was called ATM for Apollo Telescope Mount. It was to be a battery of telescopes mounted in the equipment bay of an Apollo spacecraft, operated by the astronauts, and doing solar observing. If the craft could remain in orbit for two weeks, they would be able to observe the sun through half a solar revolution. Lindsay was fighting very hard to convince Harry Goett and headquarters of the feasibility of the mission.

Hogarth had been having headaches with another powerful and temperamental university, this time the Massachusetts Institute of Technology. M.I.T. had been invited to join the OSO-C mission, and its response had been extremely cool. Hogarth said, "There were two problems. In the first place, the M.I.T. group was one of those that felt it should have a satellite all to itself. Secondly, there had been differences with some NASA people over another matter. To add to the excitement, the M.I.T. group itself consisted of two components, and it was evident that at that marriage there had been a shotgun in the background."

Hogarth took a deep breath and made his first visit to M.I.T. There, he says, he was received with a striking and quite unprecedented speech of non-welcome from the assembled scientists. Hogarth thought, what the hell, and gave them a frank piece of his mind. To his amazement the group announced that he was so candid and honest that it would go along with him as project manager and join the mission. A deal was worked out. M.I.T. got two wheel compartments, with the dividing rib removed, and promised to conform to normal NASA procedures. But now BBRC was faced with the problem of trying to balance a lopsided satellite.

John Roach, the BBRC project engineer on OSO, says, "M.I.T. *is* rather pompous, but this is true of all the universities. All of them would like to have their own satellites. They don't like to compromise and live by the rules. They hate the Pert system. They rebel at being involved with big programs. They want to be their own boss, but they must compromise."

JPL had launched Mariners III and IV. Mariner III was sent up in November, 1964, with an Atlas booster and an Agena second stage. The nose cone imploded and did not come off the craft, and Mariner III is out there somewhere in space, still shrouded in its protective cover. Mariner IV was given a perfect launch three weeks later, and was on such an accurate trajectory for Mars that only one of the two planned midcourse maneuvers was needed for correction. Its magnificent encounter with Mars seven months later was to be one of the great triumphs of JPL's superb engineers.

Whereas Goddard builds some of its spacecraft inhouse, JPL's engineers only build prototypes; they leave the series production to industry. The first four of the seven Surveyors were being built by Hughes Aircraft. The Surveyor mission was for engineering purposes, and the first four were merely intended to prove that a soft landing on the moon was possible. JPL figured the odds were one in four of a successful soft landing.

The landing of Luna 9 on the moon in early 1966, after five previous failures, proved that the odds were even tougher than JPL had calculated. It must be pointed out that the Russian probe did not make a soft landing. Their spherical craft came down hard, with shock absorbers soaking up the impact, which may, in part, have accounted for its inability to transmit more than a dozen pictures of the lunar surface. It was still up to the Surveyor mission to prove out the soft-landing concept. The design called for a landing at approximately paratrooper landing speed.

JPL was flabbergasted and delighted when Surveyor I upset all the odds and made a perfect soft landing on the very first try in June, 1966, and transmitted thousands of pictures of the lunar surface. It was a tremendous step forward for the Apollo mission, for which Surveyor was pioneering.

Rangers VII and VIII had had their spectacular successes, and their closeups of the moon had already thrilled the world. Ranger IX was down at the Cape being readied for its launch, but JPL was furious because Gemini was being scheduled for the same week, and it was impossible for the launch and tracking people to take care of the two missions back to back. "Damn it!" the Ranger team was swearing. "Why in hell can't Gemini wait a week? It doesn't make any difference to them when they shoot, but we *have* to go next week." Ranger couldn't stand down because their launch "window" was limited. Let me explain the window concept.

You are looking down on the earth from above the North Pole. The sun is at the top of this page, some distance beyond twelve o'clock. The moon is revolving around the earth in a counterclockwise orbit. Now, when you shoot the moon, you have to lead it with your craft; you don't have the velocity or maneuverability to catch up with it and hit the target. You must aim for a point in space ahead of the moon. The moon comes trundling along in its orbit as the probe arrives a little ahead of it, and the craft is drawn down to the leading face of the moon by the attraction of gravity. *Leading face* is the crux. You always have to aim to the left of the moon. Then lunar gravity brings you down on a slant to the right to its leading face.

When you have a new moon at twelve o'clock, with the sun behind it, the entire face is dark, and your cameras can't photograph anything. So that's out. When the moon is in the first quarter at nine o'clock, its leading face is still turned away from the sun and is dark, so that's out, too. At full moon at six o'clock, the entire face is illuminated by the sun, but since it's facing the sun directly, it has no shadows, which makes it worthless for geographic and geological analysis of the photographs. You base your interpretation on the appearance of shadows.

That leaves the third quarter at three o'clock, when the leading face of the moon is turned toward the sun. Therefore your window is a period of six days. But this can be reduced to smaller windows, depending on what you want to photograph. Ranger IX was intended to photograph the crater Alphonsus. This meant that the launch window was one hour in the afternoon of March 21. The sunset line was creeping across the moon's face toward Alphonsus. If they launched after the twenty-first, the crater would be too deep in shadows to reveal anything to the cameras by the time the Ranger probe arrived. If they launched before the twenty-first, the sun would still be too high above the crater when the probe arrived, and the photographs wouldn't show enough shadows.

JPL wanted the Gemini mission to stand down but couldn't see how they could possibly make the request. This was not only the first manned flight in eighteen months, but the first two-man flight in NASA's history, and it was receiving tremendous news coverage. Dr. Pickering flew to Washington to see what compromise could be arranged, while the Ranger team fumed and resigned itself to waiting a month for another window. Fortunately, or tactfully, Gemini developed technical difficulties and was forced to delay for a week, so it all ended happily with two triumphant missions.

Now back to Goddard. On his way to the conference, Hogarth is having an informal discussion with John Roach, the BBRC project engineer. They're discussing OSO-II and OSO-C. Hogarth asks, "On orbit 452 was Hallam turned on?"

"No. Chubb was."

"Did you get an all-channel report?"

"Yes. It was very good. Housekeeping was good, too. On 452 we had a dump of all data. Chubb got three raster scans on 451, and two of them were very good."

"But Hallam wants a report on 453 and we've got to give him a print-out."

"Can do."

"Was Hallam on in 450?"

"Yes."

"Did he interfere with Tousey?"

"No, not significantly. As a matter of fact, when Tousey saw his results on 450, he smiled."

"Yes. Chubb saw the sun yesterday. He's convinced it's really there now."

"Well, it's a quiet sun and there isn't much, except for one flare."

"John, why isn't a backup command system wired into C? Off the record, C will be late. If it is late, can we wire in a backup command system?"

"Ball Brothers are scared to death of it."

"Yes, but they were scared to death of two thousand pounds gas pressure. Then maybe we'd better launch C with the transmitter off. We can get along with Doppler tracking."

"But if the antenna arms don't go up, we're in trouble."

"We can always issue a command."

"Yeah, but we won't know where it is to command it."

"Well, the Russians will know. Now, John, about that new junk we have to install in C . . ."

"You mean that high-price junk?"

"Yes. Now, we've got the money, but you'll have to build it."

"Fair enough. You have the money; we have the time."

"You haven't got much."

"That's true, but we'll get moving on it. We'll make it a crash program."

"Right. We'll give you sixty-five thousand dollars. Now, on the ground command verifier; we should have five for all the tracking stations. After all, Syncom I blew up. They gave a command and it disappeared. But do we really need five? My feeling is we don't. What we have to do is drill our crews so we won't run the risk of sending a wrong command and destroying the thing. What we should do is install just one at Fort Myers, and then if these Tracking and Data characters destroy the bird, they're hung."

(Later, Hogarth's ground command verifier precaution was thrown out of the budget by management for reasons of economy.)

Hogarth and Roach enter the conference room in Building One, and the experimenters' meeting begins. Let's join it at the same moment that we did when this history of the OSO family began. This time I'll report the dialogue fully. Just to refresh your memory, here is the cast of characters, not in the order of appearance:

Solar Ultraviolet Spectrophotometer and Spectroheliograph — Dr. Reeves
Solar Coronagraph and Solar Ultraviolet Spectroheliograph — Dr. Tousey
Solar X-Ray Telescopes and Solar X-Ray Spectroheliographs — Dr. Chubb
Celestial Ultraviolet Spectrophotometer — Dr. Hallam
Zodiacal Light Telescopes — Dr. Ney
Solar Gamma-Ray Telescope — Mr. Frost
Celestial Gamma-Ray Telescope — Dr. Leavitt
Celestial Irradiation Monitor — Mr. Neel
Project Manager — Laurence Hogarth
Project Scientist — Dr. John Lindsay
BBRC Project Engineer — John Roach
Various staff assistants, mission coordinators, and tracking and data representatives.

TOUSEY: We're having difficulties with the Van Allen belt. We're getting too much noise. It may be from dust or snowflakes, the same that were photographed in rocket experiments three years ago. Also, the telescope objective is fluorescing. We don't know why.

HOGARTH: Could it be from the sun?

TOUSEY: It couldn't be from the sun. We weren't locked on the sun long enough. It might be from the Van Allen belt and Starfish.

HOGARTH: What lens was used?

AN ASSISTANT: I don't remember the glass number, but it was a special crown spectacle glass selected for minimum fluorescence.

HOGARTH: Have you correlated the fluorescent effect with the Van Allen belt?

ASSISTANT: We haven't reduced our data sufficiently to tell.

TOUSEY: Now, about the spectroheliograph. We're getting random and unwanted switching from wavelength to wavelength during raster scans. We don't know why. Most of the time it's rastering nicely, but there are times when it slips in azimuth and elevation. [To assistant] Will you show them, please? [The assistant goes to the blackboard, chalks a circle for the sun, and then starts to draw the horizontal lines of the raster scan from top to bottom. But some of the lines fail to reach all the way from one edge of the disc to the other, and just below the center of the disc the scan abruptly leaps up to the top and starts its erratic course again.]

HOGARTH: Did this happen when the raster was on alone?

TOUSEY: Never. It happens when the photomultiplier is on.

LINDSAY: I don't see how this can happen from the raster scan generator circuitry.

THE ASSISTANT: Subcom extra pulses force the raster to jump, and then it tries to get back into sync again.

HOGARTH: Are the words that print out elevation and azimuth reliable?

THE ASSISTANT: Yes. They give us a real-time position of the sun.

TOUSEY: The spectroheliograph alignment is not perfect. It's off by three minutes in azimuth and four minutes in altitude. We have no idea why except that the instrument was shaken up in the launch.

LINDSAY: I remember you had some trouble with the filter during tests. Did you leave it in?

TOUSEY: Yes. Why?

LINDSAY: I was wondering if it was shifted as a result of the centrifugal force of the spin-up, and that might account for the different levels of your readings.

TOUSEY: It's an idea. You may be right. [He sits down.]

HALLAM: My photomultiplier and counters are being saturated by the Van Allen radiation and go dead at periods.

NEY: I'm not having that trouble with my scintillation counter. It's rock-steady.

HALLAM: Also, we don't have continuity of data. We only get data on the Fort Myers passes.

HOGARTH: Well, we have a direct line from Fort Myers to Goddard. The South American stations haven't forwarded the data they've received yet.

HALLAM: Another thing, we're getting meaningless words which have nothing to do with the experiment. They haven't been asked for, and they don't seem to affect the subsequent sequence of the data.

AN ASSISTANT: On one orbit we got five readouts of sixty-three.

LINDSAY: Does anyone else use sixty-three in his experiment? Has anybody looked at the all-channel print-out of the first ten orbits? What I had in mind was the possibility of the attitude of the experiment in the Van Allen belt being responsible for data difficulties . . . that is, the electromagnetic field in one particular position might do it.

NEY: Also hot spots in the Van Allen belt; but I'm not having that trouble.

LINDSAY: The only conclusion I can make is that Ed's experiment isn't working. He doesn't see the Van Allen belt. He doesn't get any noise. He just gets results.

NEY: We get more trouble from plankton radiation than anything else.

ROACH: Is there any correlation between line errors in the transmission from Fort Myers to Goddard and the anomalies? The errors are computed before and after every pass.

HOGARTH: It's worth looking into.

NEY: For me everything's working fine, except that we're playing a kind of space roulette because there's always a chance that the sail will obscure our telescopes. You can spot these events in the data readout, and they average normal, about one in five.

CHUBB: I'm sorry to report that when Hallam's experiment is on and Tousey's is off, our results are ruined. The same thing happens when Tousey is on and Hallam is off. I suggest that we turn off all the experiments and then switch them on, separately and in sequence, to find out what the cause and the relationship is.

NEY: You guys ought to quit trying to do these hard experiments that are significant. You ought to do the ones that don't mean a damn thing, but are easy.

HOGARTH: Dr. Reeves?

REEVES: We had an arc, a short-duration pulse, that blew the electronics.

LINDSAY: What makes you think you had an arc?

REEVES: We had high-count readings immediately on turn-on which died away. Rather than arc, call it a high-voltage breakdown.

HOGARTH: But you must have an atmosphere for arcing.

REEVES: Yes.

HOGARTH: Where do you think it took place?

REEVES: In or near the photomultiplier.

HOGARTH: What would make a photomultiplier arc?

REEVES: Gas pressure. Contamination of dust or material. Ions inside the box.

HOGARTH: Was the equipment potted?

REEVES: No.

HOGARTH: Was the cabling open?

REEVES: At three points. It was all insulated, but unshielded at three places. [An assistant goes to the blackboard and diagrams the circuitry.]

HOGARTH: How much testing did it get?

REEVES: All of B-I's, including the Terminal-3 test at the Cape. It was removed from the B and flown in the II. It never arced in the tests. It was thermal-vacuum tested and accepted, and shake-tested and accepted.

LINDSAY: Was there any material used on the terminals that might have whiskered?

REEVES: No. We used a number of materials and they were all silver-soldered. None of them were likely to whisker. There might have been a mechanical failure in the photomultiplier, a wire shaken loose and crossed. Or, the photomultiplier is magnetic and a bit of metal filing might have been shaken loose by the launch and attracted to the photomultiplier. There might have been ions or electrons inside the box where they caused the high voltage to arc, but I don't see how at that high vacuum. There might have been a photoelectric yield from metals as a result of photoemission from sunlight.

LINDSAY: Would the buildup of magnetic and dielectric dust particles on a terminal be enough to create an arc?

REEVES: Yes. It only has to happen once, and then a carbon path is established.

HOGARTH: We'll adjourn for lunch now. We'll meet again at one o'clock sharp, gentlemen. Try to be back by one-thirty.

On the way to the cafeteria, Roach said quietly, "Harvard had a history of high-voltage trouble with their experiment. It really wasn't their fault. They lost their key electronics expert. He came down with a brain tumor."

"To date we've lost five men on the OSO program," Hogarth said. "The three killed at the Cape, the Harvard man, and Broder at White Sands."

"Harvard was involved in that, too, weren't they?"

"Yes. They sent up a sounding rocket to test the Harvard experiment to see if it really worked. It was essential to recover it. The rocket went up, the package parachuted down and was lost. Broder undertook to find it. He spent three weeks exploring the terrain in a plane and finally did locate it, but by that time he was strained and extremely depressed. He died of a heart attack a few days later."

"Harvard will fly again on OSO-D," Roach told me. "The same experiment, but improved."

"Heaven help us," Hogarth exclaimed. "It'll turn into another crash program. That's the history of NASA." He turned to me. "Do you know what a crash program is? It's getting nine women pregnant in the hope of having a baby in a month."

16

The Death Toll Mounts

A MONTH after the OSO-II Experimenters' meeting, Lindsay and Hogarth left for Europe, and conferences with the English, French, and Italian experimenters who were scheduled to participate in future OSO missions. Both men needed a holiday very badly. OSO-C was scheduled for launch in August, but had encountered exasperating difficulties. Although it was a good spacecraft and had performed very well in tests, they were having trouble with communications. Goddard had just installed a new control center, the size of a Broadway theater, to accommodate visiting dignitaries, and its switchboard had kinks which garbled the electronic conversations with the craft.

Lindsay had a pointed experiment aboard C, and had been forced to drive himself extra hard to meet the schedule. He had driven his engineers so remorselessly that one of them had collapsed and died of a heart attack. In addition, the Advanced OSO was in trouble. The mission was sick, and no one knew why. Since spacecraft creation is an art, it's often impossible to put your finger on the source of trouble. Lindsay was fretting himself into a fever trying to get AOSO straightened out.

Hogarth first became aware of how ill Lindsay had become when they were in Florence strolling along the Lungarno one evening, on their way to a restaurant. The river and the city were beautiful in the luminous twilight, but Lindsay could only talk about the problems of procurement. This was something he had always refused to discuss at Goddard; he never became involved in the business trivia of satellite building. Hogarth was amused to see that some of the project manager in himself had rubbed off on Lindsay, but was depressed when he realized that his friend had lost his capacity for enjoyment.

In Bologna they made a special side trip to see the historic university, and all through the sightseeing Lindsay was talking about photomultipliers. His mind was back home, immersed in detail. At last Hogarth turned to him and said, very gently, "John, you're sick." Lindsay began to shake. He burst out, "But it's my life!"

They returned to Goddard in May to plunge back into their difficulties. OSO-II had developed an unexpected eccentricity which was threatening its life in space. Although the satellite had been thoroughly depermed before launch, it had somehow acquired a new magnetic field which was being attracted by the earth's magnetic field. This torque caused the craft to pitch up and down. The theory was that possibly the shock and vibration of the launch had remagnetized OSO in the same way that an iron bar can be magnetized with a hammer blow at one end.

The danger was that the craft was attempting to correct every pitch motion with its gas jets, and would exhaust its gas supply prematurely. Carl Westman, one of Hogarth's aides, had been a jet pilot during the war, and he came up with a novel suggestion. Why not cut off the automatic gas system and let him pilot the craft on a real-time basis, only using the jets to correct the pitch angle when it was absolutely necessary? Hogarth agreed, and Westman went to work. He was able to extend OSO-II's life for an extra three months.

After a total of nine months and three days of operation, the pitch control gas supply was exhausted. On November 6, 1965, during Orbit 4120, OSO-II was placed in a "stow" condition. All systems except the spin control, temperature probes, receivers, and decoders were turned off. This produced a minimum drain on the batteries. Subsequent interrogations of OSO revealed that its slowly changing attitude in space will permit its batteries to recharge for a period of about two weeks every four months. This would enable the experiments to make periodic returns of data.

However there weren't many left. Harvard's ultraviolet spectrometer, which had been turned on during Orbit 14, lasted for twenty seconds. Dr. Chubb's X-ray telescope and spectroheliograph started transmitting zeros by Orbit 500 (they had nothing more to say) and were turned off. Dr. Tousey's coronagraph and spectroheliograph lasted until Orbit 1250. Then the coronagraph drive motor burned out, and the spectroheliograph became radiation saturated. Dr. Hallam's uv stellar and nebular spectrophotometer in the wheel started generating zeros on Orbit 3020, and was turned off. Evidently Dr. Chubb's point, made during the experimenters' meeting, that he, Hallam, and Tousey were lousing each other, had been well taken. The cause of the destructive interface has not yet been found.

The rest of the wheel experiments—Frost's solar gamma-ray telescope, Ney's zodiacal light monitoring, Leavitt's celestial gamma-ray telescope, and the Ames Emissivity experiment—all operated normally during the life of OSO-II and acquired data from about 99 per cent of the orbits.

Politics were getting hot at Goddard. NASA headquarters was determined to make its two most independent centers, Goddard and JPL, conform to management philosophy, and was bringing pressure on both. Headquarters insisted on having a voice in all operations. Harry Goett stood on his record, over thirty-five successful launches of major spacecraft, and refused to make the slightest concession. He was delivering exactly what he had been asked to deliver, and he wanted no kibitzers.

Lindsay backed him. Not only was Harry Goett his friend, but Lindsay was also fighting for the survival of his solar research program. He was afraid it might get lost in the shuffle of more glamorous missions. He and Hogarth had already received intimations of what NASA might have in store for them. First the command verifier precaution had been blocked; then a flight spare for OSO-C had been canceled, also for reasons of economy. When Lindsay and Hogarth thought of the money being poured into the Manned Spacecraft program, they got hot.

OSO-C was ready for launch by the latter part of August, 1965. In addition to Lindsay's X-ray spectrometer it carried eight more experiments measuring, among other things, solar uv radiation (Air Force Cambridge lab), X-radiation (University of Michigan and University of California), cosmic rays (University of Rochester), and the earth's albedo, or reflectivity (Ames Research Center). The major experiment in the wheel was M.I.T.'s double-compartment package which was a gamma-ray telescope using scintillators monitored by fifteen photomultipliers.

Lindsay, Hogarth, the experimenters and the engineers gathered in the new Goddard control center to watch the launch. The vehicle was a three-stage Delta rocket. The booster functioned perfectly, cut off, and was separated. The second stage ignited, burned, and cut off. The craft was now in its Parking Orbit and was programmed for a fifteen-second wait while the second stage was separated from the third stage, which would then ignite and insert the craft into orbit.

The control center was appalled when the illuminated displays showed that the third stage had ignited immediately after the second stage cutoff. There was no fifteen-second delay; the second stage had not had time to separate. The reports from the downrange tracking stations as far as Ascension Island came in rapidly. They were picking up OSO-C as it came over their radar fences. But it was not picked up at Johannesburg, the next station in the craft's path. The third stage had been forced to drag the second stage along with it, and had lost the thrust necessary to insert the satellite into orbit. OSO-C ended up in the South Atlantic.

"Now we've got an OSO-Sea Observatory," Carl Westman muttered. Not with a bang but a wisecrack.

Vehicle failure is a far more tragic way of losing a craft than something happening in flight. Lindsay was crushed. Everyone was dazed. Hogarth struggled up out of his own despair and assumed an air of cool confidence. He told them that everything was not yet lost, and called an immediate meeting of all staffs. By midnight they'd decided that there was a way of scraping up enough material to refit for a re-flight, despite the fact that there was no backup for C.

They completed the general scheme the next day. All the experimenters were still at Goddard, and before they left Hogarth made them sign sworn statements that they had experiment spares. By the end of the week the detailed proposal was complete. There were discussions at Goddard and headquarters for another week. The pressure was great and passions were high. Hogarth said that he believed his life expectancy was shortened by 19 per cent, but three weeks after the failure of OSO-C, approval for a re-flight in July 1966, came from headquarters.

The strongest opposition came from the experimenters aboard OSO-D, which had been scheduled for a launch in that same month, but which now would have to be put down until November, 1966. Hogarth confronted them and argued, "Look, suppose *you* went into the drink. Wouldn't you want the men after you to stand down and give you another chance? We can't rob these men of three years of their productive life." They finally agreed. Later it developed that the experimenters aboard D who had complained the loudest wouldn't have been ready in July anyway.

As if the failure of OSO-C wasn't bad enough, Lindsay received another shattering blow. In late summer of 1965 Harry Goett lost his fight with headquarters. It was an ironic defeat. Goett wanted no part of headquarters interfering with Goddard? Very good; he was promoted to a desk at headquarters. In other words, he was kicked upstairs. He had one year to go to retirement and was tempted to sit it out grimly, but a pension compromise was arranged and he left NASA to join Philco as director of the New Products Division.

With Goett's departure, the atmosphere at Goddard turned ugly, and everything degenerated into a Madison Avenue intrigue. Splinter groups formed, dissolved, and re-formed. The top men were in an armed truce because no one knew who was going to be elevated to Harry Goett's job. In fact, no one ever was. The directorate was revised into the headquarters pattern of a triumvirate, with Dr. John Clark as acting director, Dr. John Townsend as deputy director, and Mr. Eugene Wasielewski, an engineer, as associate director. The era of the individual was over; Management preferred a committee. NASA felt that the leadership and independence for which Goett had been hired was no longer needed. The organization which he helped create now needed organization men.

Unfortunately for Lindsay, the organization men were brought in in new layers above him which, he said, demoted him. Many others at Goddard had the same reaction, and there was much heartbreak. Lindsay couldn't stand what he called "the lowering ceiling at Goddard," but he had never been a man of action, and didn't know what to do about it. He began to regret not having taken other jobs which had been offered to him. He considered going back to the University of North Carolina to teach. He even hinted around that he would like the job of assistant director at Goddard, but he was unequipped for management, and everybody knew it. He began to fall to pieces.

In the middle of September, 1965, he was working in his office in Building 2 at Goddard when he suffered a sudden, severe heart attack. It was totally unexpected; he had never had a history of heart trouble. Lindsay weathered it alone. After the seizure was over, he dragged himself to Hogarth's office and told him all about it. He was genuinely frightened. Hogarth was deeply concerned.

"John," he said, "you've got to see a good doctor at once. I suggest you see mine. You drink thirteen cups of coffee a day and smoke like a chimney. Maybe you've just had a minor attack, like me, or maybe it's serious, but see a doctor at once."

Lindsay nodded, said that he would, and left. Hogarth never knew whether he did or not, or whether he even told his wife about the attack. "He never let his right hand know what his left hand was doing."

Less than two weeks later, on September 26, a bright Sunday, Lindsay went out to mow the lawn in front of his house. His wife was busy inside, but she could hear the mower putt-putting away. Sometime later, she glanced out a front window and saw Lindsay lying face down on the grass, with the mower still running alongside him. He was dead.

Mrs. Lindsay was in an agony, wondering how long he'd been lying there. She was afraid that if she'd found him sooner she might have been able to save him. But one of the neighbors who gathered to help was a registered nurse. She said that it had been a massive heart attack, and he had died instantly.

Everyone at Goddard was shocked and saddened; Hogarth most of all. "He was my only friend at Goddard, and I feel his loss very deeply. John was a damned hard fellow to help. He didn't kid himself, for one thing, and the man who faces facts, who can't delude himself, leads a damned hard life. John did. I do. He couldn't persuade himself that things were going to be all right, even when they were. I could see they were, but I could never make him believe it.

He *could* have achieved recognition doing what he was doing at Goddard, but he didn't believe it."

Lindsay left unfinished the Advanced Orbiting Solar Observatory, the Apollo Telescope Mount, and the OSO satellites C through H. Three months after his death the White House announced that AOSO had been canceled because of the rising costs of the war in Vietnam. The mission team was disappointed but relieved. The mission had been sick, and this was a bailout. The AC-4 Centaur, which blew up at the Cape, had been sick in the same indefinable way, and everyone had known it. But so much talent, time, and money had gone into it that NASA was forced to go through with the project, keeping its fingers crossed. Now AOSO was off the hook and nothing would be lost, because its experiments would be transferred to improved OSO's and ATM, the Apollo Telescope Mount.

Lindsay's dedication and persuasion lived on after him, for headquarters approved the ATM provisionally in early 1966. For the first time it will be possible for a man to make observations with a high-quality telescope in space. He will be briefed and trained by the ground astronomers, but the astronaut will use his own judgment in space during the mission. Dual X-ray telescopes and a coronagraph are contemplated, but the particular payload has not yet been selected. NASA is considering flying more ordinary telescopes for stellar work later on.

The Langley, Houston, and Huntsville Centers were asked to submit proposals for the design and construction of ATM, along with Goddard. This will give the Manned Spacecraft people at Houston their first chance to do genuine scientific work, if they get it. Goddard would like to share the mission with Houston. Houston knows nothing about scientific satellites; Goddard knows nothing about manned spacecraft; it would be an ideal collaboration.

The OSO missions must and will continue without Lindsay. He has been replaced by one of his assistants, William A. White, as acting chief of Solar Physics. White was a great admirer of John's, and feels his own inadequacy as a replacement very keenly. He also recognizes the dangers of his job. "NASA is on a par with any other industry when it comes to heart attacks." But the OSO missions have been particularly fatal. To date there have been seven human and two satellite deaths, and no one knows how many more there will be. The space program is no ivory tower for recluse types. It's a tough and killing war.

17

The Space Debate

HERE is the NASA budget for 1965 in millions of dollars:

NASA headquarters	1023.1
Ames Research Center	41.9
Electronics Research Center	1.0
Flight Research Center	6.9
Goddard Space Flight Center	300.5
Kennedy Space Center	62.1
Langley Research Center	76.9
Manned Spacecraft Center	1164.2
Marshall Space Flight Center	1232.1
Pacific Launch Operations	.1
Space Nuclear Propulsion	38.3
Western Operations Office	160.6
Wallops Station	5.2
Construction of Facilities	262.9
Operations	623.5

Add another $250 million for the Jet Propulsion Laboratory, which is chartered and financed by NASA, but is a subsidiary of the California Institute of Technology, and the total comes to five and a half billion dollars spent on the space program. This total was the same in 1966, and will increase in the succeeding years. The question most often asked is: Is it worth it?

You drive through slum areas and you think how that amount of money could transform a million shacks and hovels into decent homes. You see kids scratching around desperately, trying to raise the money to go to college, and you realize that the NASA budget could finance a million students, or close to twenty-five per cent of the total enrollment. Wouldn't the money be better spent on housing, education, hospitals, and medical research? Is the space program worth it?

There are many points of view. Ask the political representatives of the twenty states receiving the bulk of the benefits from the NASA budget, and they seriously question the wisdom of so much spending, except in their own states. Those states which are not sharing complain bitterly about their neglect, and the Department of Defense is maintaining dozens of costly and useless installations in them to placate them.

Ask the thirty-three thousand people directly employed by NASA, and they reply that they don't benefit from the spending at all. They're government employees, and government employees are notoriously underpaid. They point out that when Harry Goett was director of the Goddard Space Flight Center, and solely responsible for the spending of a million dollars a day, he received a salary of twenty thousand dollars a year. Madison Avenue advertising moguls with one-tenth of his responsibility earn ten times his salary.

Ask economists whether the space program isn't really a

gigantic pump-priming and featherbedding operation, and they answer of course it is, but add that our entire national economy is based on pump-priming and featherbedding. We only see the latter nakedly exposed in the trade unions' desperate fight against automation to protect jobs, but there is hardly a business or profession that does not practice featherbedding in one form or another. Without it, our economy would collapse. This answer does not satisfy the artist.

Ask a scientist like Bob Jastrow of the Institute for Space Studies, and he replies, "The principle motivation for the space program is not scientific at all, but a deep-felt conviction of the people that it's an important step for our country to take. I deflect the word 'adventure' because it's associated with adventurers, and adventurers don't get five billion dollars.

"Today we're on the threshold of an extraordinary step in the direction of the control of the entire solar system. In this context it's extremely conservative to say that it doesn't have to be done immediately.

"It's exciting that the United States is willing to spend five billion dollars a year without any promise of immediate tangible results. The spur that's pushed us is competition with the Russians, but the results have been magnificently beneficial. This is not a scientific program, therefore, but it's a program that identifies with the national will and interest in the deepest sense."

Laurence Hogarth says, "I, as an engineer, ask the question and have never received a satisfactory answer. What we have now is consumers of raw data from space. The next step is people who will be interested in the effect of this data. The pure scientist keeps his eyes in the boat; that's his job. Our job is to get him up there. What must happen is that the utilization of this data must become the concern of another group of people.

"It's useless to talk to scientists about this. They can go on very happily, building more complicated packages, writing papers about them, and traveling around the world to meetings and admiring each other. By the very nature of their work they must be compartmentalized. We need people who can sit back, take a broad view, and look for significance. It's important to make the space program significant. We must get beyond tactics to strategy.

"Think of this: the sun is a huge thermonuclear reaction. Every scientist who is a solar physicist is really looking at some facet of that reaction. He has a grandstand seat at the only controlled thermonuclear reaction that we can get close to. When all the observations of all the solar physicists are in, we may well have all the pieces that we need to understand such a reaction. But at that point we need the man who can deal with all these pieces together. He will be a different kind of physicist. What we show him may well contain the answer to mankind's great energy problem."

On the space program as a pump-priming operation, Hogarth says, "NASA has an important effect on our economy, true; but you must realize that it has an even more important effect on education. It absorbs highly trained people. Until the Space Age there wasn't much demand for physicists, outside of teaching, so very few people became physicists. NASA has changed that. It fosters the first-line talent that might never have gone to college if they didn't know that there was a demand and a place for them."

The NASA officials recognize the fact that our country has other pressing needs, but put up a tough and realistic defense. They say, "You can't lick something with nothing; you have to come up with a program. If there's anybody who thinks the money should be spent on something else, let them come up with a concrete proposal. If they did come up with it, Congress would probably give it to them. If anybody thinks NASA is getting too much money, don't just tell Congress to give us less; *compete* for it." This answer does not please the do-gooders.

To the pragmatist who wants to know what return we're getting on our investment or, as one asked, "When are we going to find pay dirt in the sky?" there are many answers. Harry Goett said, "Here's a ghoulish thought. Many of the great advances in medicine, communications, and transport came from World War I and World War II, which provided motivation. I think of the space program as being a good kind of war. The space program provides this kind of motivation."

Other apologists offer other rewards; accurate weather forecasts which will be of vital importance to business, exobiology which will throw tremendous light on cell chemistry and disease and may pioneer a cure for cancer, and the advanced techniques of satellite construction which will improve the mechanical systems we use in everyday life and make them more reliable.

J. O. Simpson, chief of Systems Design at BBRC, says, "NASA is teaching American manufacturers the meaning of quality control, and improving their standards. There'll be a feedback; your wife's iron will work better. People may not notice it, but it will happen. We'll see this in TV sets, which have been lousy up to now, and there's been no excuse for this. This will be the biggest feedback of all."

But these are specious answers. The only real answer is Harry Goett's "Have faith," and do-gooders are impatient with this. They regard NASA as a gaggle of bright boys with unlimited allowance, playing with the biggest damn chemistry set in the world.

Our space program isn't a game, it's a magnificent gamble, and the trouble with do-gooders is that they're too sincere to understand the challenge of a gamble. It's true we may lose the bet. It happened before with the dirigible program that went bust with the *Shenandoah, Macon,* and *Akron* disasters. God knows how much money went down the drain with those experiments. Now all that's left is a Goodyear blimp hovering over ball games.

We do know how much money is being spent on the space program; more importantly, we know we can afford it. All we can do is cross our fingers and hope that the bet will pay off. We must back our bright boys. We must have faith in discovery. As Ben Franklin said to the cynic who wanted to know what the practical use of a new invention was, "Sir, what is the use of a newborn child?"

Perhaps the most curious aspect of the debate is the clash between the members of the humanities and the members of the scientific disciplines. An atmosphere of antipathy, sometimes downright hatred, has been created, and has been much discussed by Aldous and Julian Huxley, C. P. Snow, and many others. I happen to have been educated in both the humanities and the disciplines, so I have a foot in each camp. I'm sorry to report that it's the members of the humanities alone who are creating the hostility with fossil attitudes.

The common impression is that scientists and engineers are our enemies, directly responsible for all the exasperations of modern living. They are regarded as insensitive creatures with no appreciation for the finer things in life, so obsessed with science and technology that they are destroying all our amenities. But this is an old-fashioned attitude, created by the caricatures of scientists and engineers drawn by Jules Verne, H. G. Wells, Conan Doyle, and Karel Čapek.

We must modernize our thinking about these men; they're an altogether different breed today. When Arthur Fiedler came to Huntsville with the Boston Symphony to give a concert, he was invited to meet Wernher von Braun. Fiedler was delighted, but frightened. What could a conductor talk about to an engineer? He was enchanted to discover that when von Braun was a young student he had been a pupil of Paul Hindemith, Fiedler's favorite composer, and they spent a lively afternoon discussing music and rockets.

Very often the scientists and engineers are lovers of the arts, and sympathize with the humanities, as witness Dr. Al Hibbs's remark about sending poets rather than pilots into space. It's the poets who reject the space age. They ask, "Why go into space when a sonnet can tell you all you want to know about the universe?" I'm saddened by this antagonism because it's the poets who should give the intuitive answer to the question: Is the space program worth the money?

Watching the delicate artistry with which spacecraft are fashioned, trembling at the drama of their launches, admiring the exquisite curves of their trajectories, listening to their strange voices speaking from millions of miles away, stretching the imagination to envision the new concepts of space, you realize that this is twentieth-century poetry, an unheard-of poetry of tremendous dimensions. And who questions the cost of a poem?

Selected Bibliography

Adams, Carsbie C., and Wernher Von Braun: *Careers in Astronautics and Rocketry*, N.Y., McGraw-Hill, 1962.

Ahnstrom, D. N.: *The Complete Book of Jets and Rockets*, Cleveland, World, Rev. 1959.

Alexander, Tom: *Project Apollo*, N.Y., Dial, 1963.

Asimov, Isaac: *Satellites in Outer Space*, N.Y., Random House, Rev. 1964.

Beauchamp, Wilbur L., et al.: *Science Is Explaining*, Chicago, Scott Foresman and Company, 1963.

Bell, Joseph N.: *Seven Into Space*, N.Y., Hawthorn, 1960.

Bergaust, Erik: *Reaching for the Stars*, N.Y., Doubleday, 1960.

———: *Saturn Story*, N.Y., Putnam, 1962.

———: *Rocket City, U.S.A.*, N.Y., Macmillan, 1963.

Berkner, Lloyd V., and Hugh Odishaw, editors: *Science in Space*, N.Y., McGraw-Hill, 1961.

Binder, Otto O.: *Victory in Space*, N.Y., Walker, 1962.

Bondi, Hermann: *The Universe at Large*, N.Y., Doubleday, 1960.

Boyd, R. L. F.: *Space Research by Rocket and Satellite*, N.Y., Harper, 1961.

Branley, Franklin M.: *Exploring by Astronaut: The Story of Project Mercury*, N.Y., Crowell, 1961.

Brinley, Bertrand R.: *Rocket Manual for Amateurs*, N.Y., Ballantine, U6011.

Burgess, Eric: *Satellites and Spacecraft*, N.Y., Macmillan, 1960.

Butler, S. T., and H. Messel: *The Universe of Time and Space*, N.Y., Macmillan, 1963.

Canby, Courtlandt: *A History of Rockets and Space*, N.Y., Hawthorn, 1963.

Carpenter, M. Scott, et al.: *We Seven, by the Astronauts Themselves*, N.Y., Simon & Schuster, 1962.

Clarke, Arthur C.: *Interplanetary Flight*, N.Y., Harper, 1960.

———: *Profiles of the Future*, N.Y., Harper, 1962.

Cole, D. M., and D. W. Cox: *Islands in Space*, Philadelphia, Chilton, 1964.

Corliss, William: *Space Probes and Planetary Exploration*, Princeton, Van Nostrand, 1965.

Davis, Clive E.: *Messages from Space*, N.Y., Dodd Mead, 1961.

Diamond, Edwin: *The Rise and Fall of the Space Age*, N.Y., Doubleday, 1964.

Dietz, David: *All About Satellites and Space Ships*, N.Y., Random House, 1958.

Dull, Charles E., et al.: *Modern Physics*, N.Y., Holt, Rinehart, and Winston, 1963.

Elliott, L. Paul, and William F. Wilcox: *Physics — A Modern Approach*, N.Y., Macmillan, 1958.

Emme, Eugene M.: *The History of Rocket Technology*, Detroit, Wayne State University Press, 1964.

Fermi, Laura, and Gilberto Bernardini: *Galileo and the Scientific Revolution*, N.Y., Basic Books, 1961.

Fortune, Editors of: *The Space Industry: America's Newest Giant*, Englewood Cliffs, N.J., Prentice-Hall, 1962.

Gamow, George: *Gravity*, N.Y., Doubleday, 1962.

Gardner, Martin: *Science Puzzlers,* N.Y., Viking, 1960.
Glasstone, S., and N. H. Princeton: *Sourcebook on the Space Sciences,* Princeton, Van Nostrand, 1965.
Golovine, M. N.: *Conflict in Space,* N.Y., St. Martin's, 1962.
Goodwin, H. L.: *The Images of Space,* N.Y., Holt, Rinehart, and Winston, 1965.
Gottlieb, William: *Jets and Rockets and How They Work,* N.Y., Doubleday, 1959.
Haley, Andrew G.: *Rocketry and Space Exploration,* Princeton, Van Nostrand, 1958.
Hanrahan, James S., and David Bushnell: *Space Biology: The Human Factors in Space Flight,* N.Y., Basic Books, 1960.
Hogben, Lancelot: *The Wonderful World of Mathematics,* N.Y., Doubleday, 1955.
Jastrow, Robert, editor: *The Exploration of Space,* N.Y., Macmillan, 1960.
Joseph, Alexander, Paul F. Brandwein, et al.: *A Source-book for the Physical Sciences,* N.Y., Harcourt, Brace, and World, 1961.
Klee, E., and O. Merk: *The Birth of the Missile, the Secrets of Peenemuende,* N.Y., Dutton, 1965.
Knight, Clayton: *Rockets, Missiles, and Satellites,* N.Y., Grosset and Dunlap, 1962.
Levine, Sol: *Appointment in the Sky,* N.Y., Walker, 1963.
Ley, Willy: *Rockets, Missiles, and Space Travel,* N.Y., Viking, Rev. 1961.
———: *Harnessing Space,* N.Y., Macmillan, 1963.
Macvey, John W.: *Alone in the Universe?* N.Y., Macmillan, 1963.
Meitner, J. G.: *Astronautics for Science Teachers,* N.Y., Wiley, 1966.
NASA and U. S. Office of Education: *What's Up There?,* Government Printing Office, Washington, 1964.

Neurath, Marie: *Man-Made Moons,* N.Y., Lothrop, 1960.
———: *Rockets and Jets,* N.Y., Lothrop, 1961.
Newell, Homer E.: *Express to the Stars,* N.Y., McGraw-Hill, 1961.
———: *Guide to Rockets, Missiles, and Satellites,* N.Y., McGraw-Hill, 1961.
Odishaw, Hugh, editor: *The Challenges of Space,* Chicago, University of Chicago Press, 1962.
Ordway, Frederick I., James Patrick Gardner, and Mitchell R. Sharpe: *Basic Astronautics,* Englewood Cliffs, N.J., Prentice-Hall, 1962.
Ordway, Frederick I., *Life in Other Solar Systems,* N.Y., Dutton, 1965.
Ovenden, Michael W.: *Artificial Satellites,* Baltimore, Penguin, Q23, 1961.
Parker, Bertha Morris: *Rockets and Missiles,* N.Y., Row Peterson, 1961.
Parkin, Charles M., Jr.: *The Rocket Handbook for Amateurs,* N.Y., Day, 1959.
Pratt, Fletcher: *All About Rockets and Jets,* N.Y., Random House, 1955.
Purser, P. E., M. A. Faget, and N. F. Smith: *Manned Spacecraft: Engineering Design and Operation,* Stamford, Conn., Fairchild, 1964.
Sanger, Eugen: *Space Flight,* N.Y., McGraw-Hill, 1965.
Sargeant, Charles: *How to Draw Rockets and Spaceships,* N.Y., Viking, 1958.
Sells, S. B., and Charles A. Berry, M.D., editors: *Human Factors in Jet and Space Travel,* N.Y., Ronald, 1961.
Shankle, R. O.: *The Twins of Space,* Philadelphia, Lippincott, 1964.
Stine, G. Harry: *Rocket Power and Space Flight,* N.Y., Holt, Rinehart, and Winston, 1957.

Sullivan, Walter: *We Are Not Alone,* N.Y., McGraw-Hill, 1964.
Trinklein, Frederick E., and Charles M. Huffer: *Modern Space Science,* N.Y., Holt, Rinehart, and Winston, 1961.
Wiech, Raymond E., and Robert F. Strauss: *Fundamentals of Rocket Propulsion,* N.Y., Reinhold, 1960.
Willks, Willard E., *The New Wilderness,* N.Y., David McKay, 1963.

Index